TREES OF THE WESTERN PACIFIC REGION

Descriptions of some of the common and readily accessible trees of southeast Asia bordering on the Pacific Ocean and South China Sea, and of the islands of the western Pacific; including local and native names, occurrence, descriptions of the trees and characteristics of their woods.

by

J. HUGO KRAEMER, Ph.D.

Associate in Forestry, Agricultural Experiment Station, Purdue University

West Lafayette, Indiana

1951

Reprinted and Distributed by
TRI-STATE OFFSET COMPANY
817 Main Street   Cincinnati 2, Ohio

ACKNOWLEDGMENTS

The author wishes to express his sincere appreciation for the help of the following men in the preparation of this book: to Dr. E. D. Merrill, formerly Administrator of Botanical Collections, Harvard University, for review of the entire manuscript and for making available herbarium material for the illustrations; to Dr. E. H. Walker, Associate Curator, Smithsonian Institution, for review of a portion of the manuscript and for making available herbarium material for the illustrations; to Mr. L. J. Brass, Botanist, American Museum of Natural History, for review of the manuscript and for furnishing personal notes on certain trees taken during expeditions in the region; to Mr. C. D. Mell, Tropical Woods Consultant, for help during the assembly of the information; to Dr. F. W. Foxworthy, formerly Forester, Federated Malay States Government, for furnishing personal notes on certain trees and their woods in the region; and to Mr. L. R. Warthen of the Bureau of Yards and Docks, Navy Department, for his work on the drawings.

CONTENTS

INTRODUCTION

Before World War II, there was relatively little interest in, or knowledge of foreign forest resources in the United States. During the war, however, the vast far flung operations with the necessity of the construction of land bases of various types, made evident the need for knowledge of native trees and their woods. This was particularly true in the Pacific theater of operations where the native trees and woods differ so greatly from those in the United States.

The material in this book was originally assembled during the war for the use of the armed forces and the trees described are all available at low elevations, near beaches, or along water courses. Their woods vary in durability but they have desirable characteristics for a very wide variety of uses from rough construction to high grade veneers and fine cabinet work. All are widely distributed within the region.

A large amount of literature has been searched in the preparation of this book and the reference list contains only a selection from it. To the basic material has been added information from personal notes made available by men who have engaged in exploration and studies in the region. The drawings were made from herbarium material at Harvard University and at the Smithsonian Institution. This is the first time that botanical descriptions, illustrations, and descriptions of the woods of these trees have been combined and made available in American literature.

1

The region in which the trees described in this book occur, extends roughly from 25 deg. N. Lat. to 15 deg. S. Lat. and from 95 deg. to 165 deg. E. Long. It is a region of great distances, of many islands, of varied land forms and climatic conditions, and of many peoples. There are areas of sparse and scattered population in which virgin forests occur in practically untouched wilderness, but there are also areas of extreme overpopulation with consequent destruction of nearly all natural vegetation.

Whether we like it or not, our national interests and responsibilities are now no longer limited by our Atlantic and Pacific coastlines. Greater knowledge of the rest of the World is urgently needed if we are to carry out our part in World affairs in an intelligent manner. It is hoped that this book will contribute in some measure to that objective.

THE TREES OF THE REGION

The natural vegetation of the region is extremely complex. It has been estimated that there are several thousand species of trees present, occurring almost entirely in mixed forests. In many areas there are as many as 60 or 70 tree species on a single acre. Practically the only exceptions to this highly complex forest are the almost pure stands of mangrove along the shorelines, the stands of *Nothofagus* in the mountains of New Guinea, parts of the Dipterocarp region of the Philippines, and the stands of ilimo, (*Octomeles sumatrana*) in New Guinea. There are not many pure forest stands as we know them in the United States.

Much work has been done on the trees of this region, both botanically and from the standpoint of their management and utilization. This is particularly true in British Borneo, Java, the Malay States and the Philippines. However, there undoubtedly are a large number of species still unclassified. Of the trees already botanically classified, only a small proportion are presented in this book; nevertheless, 50 families, 119 genera and 178 species are represented in the descriptions.

The families are arranged according to the Engler and Prantl sequence, but the genera and species are arranged alphabetically. A brief statement of characteristics is given for each family but generic descriptions are omitted. The descriptions of species were designed to be brief and to avoid highly technical terms, but to include all the available useful information. The species described are not necessarily representative of their respective genera but were included because they are useful timber trees in the region. It was desired to have as many genera represented as possible.

Many trees of genera such as *Elaeocarpus, Cryptocarya, Eugenia* (*Syzygium*), *Vitex, Myristica, Dysoxylum*, etc., may be listed as occurring in one special locality, but the genera may contain additional tree species which occur in other areas of the Western Pacific. Several genera are very large. For example, *Eugenia* (*Syzygium*) contains at least 500 species, most of which are forest trees. *Calophyllum, Cryptocarya, Diospyros, Dysoxylum, Canarium, Elaeocarpus, Terminalia, Wormia, Myristica, Vitex, Lithocarpus, Homalium, Garcinia*, and *Planchonia* are also large genera. Many of the trees represented here would not be considered important from a commercial operation standpoint but they are distributed where the advanced bases will be built and produce wood which is suitable for all types of construction from the most temporary to semipermanent.

It will be noted that local names are included in the descriptions as well as the scientific names. In most cases these are native names as only a few of the woods in this manual are known to commerce and have received English names. Native languages show great variation. Very frequently a tribe on one side of a river may have one name for a tree species and a second tribe on the other side will have an entirely different name for the same tree or the second tribe may call another tree by the same name used by the first tribe for an entirely different species. These native names may prove highly useful but no great reliance should be placed on them until

4

the identity of each useful timber tree in the working area is well established. Scientific names are the proper and only reliable means of identifying these trees and personnel should not be afraid to use them. These botanical names are often easier to pronounce than the native ones. They must be learned and applied if any certainty is to be attached to what woods are being logged, milled, and used.

The illustrations accompanying the descriptions are approximately one-fourth natural size, and they include leaves, flowers, and fruit. Occasionally flowers and fruits have been drawn larger, and when this was done, the size was indicated on the drawing.

COLLECTION OF SAMPLES
IN THE FIELD

In the course of logging and sawmilling operations, many tree species will be cut and utilized which are not listed in this manual. In the event that outstandingly useful species are discovered, it is highly desirable that such trees be promptly identified in order that they may be fully described and this information made available to other operating units.

In order for authentic determinations of identity to be made, wood and herbarium specimens must be obtained from the tree in question. Each wood sample should be at least 2 by 2 by 4 inches, and typical pieces of the bark, sapwood, and heartwood should be obtained. These wood samples should be cut from the tree as soon as it is felled, assigned a collection number, and placed in an individual container.

At the same time that the bark and wood samples are obtained, the collection of typical herbarium material should be made and labeled with the same collection number as the bark and wood. The herbarium material should consist of a twig bearing two complete leaves, and of flowers and fruit whenever possible. Whenever fruits are not available or are so large as to make their collection impractical, they may be omitted but should be carefully described in accompanying notes. In the case of leaves, care must be taken to obtain *complete* leaves attached to the twig. This is particularly important

6

when the tree bears compound leaves. In many cases, inexperienced collectors have submitted only leaflets from compound leaves for identification. This may make identification impossible, and in any event quite difficult.

All material from the same tree should bear the same collection number. This number should be recorded in a notebook, with the date, locality of collection, local site conditions, and any additional notes on the characteristics of the tree not exhibited by the material collected.

Leaves and flowers should be pressed at once upon collection. The standard newspaper page is about 24 by 16 in. and one-half of the folded page is 12 by 16 in., which is the ideal size for pressing most of the leaves and flowers which will be encountered. Leaves and flowers may be placed out flat on a half page and the other half folded over them. In case leaves are very large, they may be bent to fit. Newspapers are recommended for this purpose since they are well suited to it, but any unglazed paper, cut to size, will do. This folder should be plainly marked with the collection number. Additional collections may be made in the same manner. A simple plant press made of two thin boards, or split bamboo woven frames, 12 by 16 in., should be constructed previous to collection. The folders with their material should be placed between these press boards as collected and the whole strapped tightly together. Blotting paper or additional sheets of newspaper should be placed between specimen folders to absorb excess moisture. A strap or rope will enable the press to be carried slung over one shoulder.

The collected material should be dried and prepared for shipment as soon as possible after collection to prevent deterioration. Upon return to camp, the press should be opened and clean, dry, absorbent blotting paper or newspaper placed between the folders, the bundle placed between press boards again, restrapped or weighted down, and the set left to dry in a spot exposed to sun and wind. The dryer sheets should be changed every few hours to facilitate the process. If corrugated cardboard cartons are available, this material, cut to size and inserted between specimen folders, will also hasten drying.

If a source of artificial heat is available, such as a large steadily operating stationary engine, the presses may be hung above it during the last stages of the drying process. If this is done, the material should be nearly dry before it is hung above the heat and care must be taken not to overheat the material, as it may become brittle.

As soon as the herbarium material is thoroughly dry, it should be protected from insects by adding some crystals of naphthalene or paradichlorobenzene to the package and sealing it up immediately in a waterproof wrapping for shipment. The first chemical is generally only an insect repellent, but the latter is a repellent and also kills any insects already on the material.

Specimens from each tree, including wood, bark and herbarium material, should be collected in *duplicate* whenever possible, that is, two complete sets of everything collected from each tree. This will aid in identification and will be of great value to the permanent collections in the United States.

THATCH MATERIALS

A variety of good roofing materials, all of them more satisfactory from the standpoint of coolness than tents and galvanized iron, are available in the region. A tent, unless it is shaded by trees or provided with a shading roof to break the rays of the sun, becomes so hot during the day that it is almost impossible to live in it. At 9,200 ft. in the New Guinea mountains, a temperature of 100°F has been recorded in an unshaded tent when the temperature under a thatched roof stood at 69°F. Brush, grass, or palm leaves, spread over a frame erected to give a clearance of a foot or two above a tent, will serve as a temporary sun roof; but for administrative use and advance field hospitals, buildings constructed in native style, with roofs that will give protection from rain as well as sun, have many advantages. The thin, stiff bark of many trees is used in mountain localities where materials easier to handle are not available. However, over most of the region, the native houses have thatched roofs and walls.

Almost any kind of broad leaf or grass found nearby in sufficient quantities is used by the natives for thatching temporary buildings such as garden houses and fishing shelters. For permanent thatch, the materials in use are palm leaves, pandanus leaves, and lalang grass. Lalang is a Malay name for *Imperata,* an erect white-plumed grass, 2 to 5 ft. high, which covers cleared land and some open country in the lowlands and in the mountain valleys.

The stiff, prickly leaves of certain species of *Pandanus*, perhaps the most durable of all the thatch materials, are used at higher elevations in the mountains. Among the numerous palms in the area, only two genera, *Nipa* and *Metroxylon*, provide thatch which is considered really durable. A well thatched roof of Nipa or Metroxylon leaf, built with a good pitch to carry off the rain, might be expected to last from about four to six years.

Nipa

The Nipa Palm (*Nipa fruticans*) is confined to river deltas and tidal swamps, where it roots in mud and silt and forms dense, pure stands in association with the mangroves, but makes its best development where the water is brackish rather than salt. This is the only palm which grows within the influence of salt or brackish water in the region. Very extensive stands are found on the deltas of some of the larger rivers. It has no stem above ground and the smooth, shining leaves are about 15 to 20 ft. long and stand more or less erect in clumps from an underground rootstock. Big round heads of fruit are produced among the leaves.

Metroxylon

In this genus are the sago palms and the ivory-nut palms. These palms form pure stands, growing in fresh-water swamps or on wet ground in the rain forests. The sago palms form extensive swamp forests on the lowlands and are found in swampy places up to elevations of 3,000 ft. or more in the mountains. The leafstalks of some forms are armed with very long, straight spines but in others they are smooth and unarmed. The plants attain about 30 to 50 ft. in height and 12 to 20 in. in diameter, are surrounded by sucker growth, and produce at maturity a great branched inflorescence from the center of the crown. These big, heavy-boled palms cannot be mistaken for anything else. They die after producing flowers and fruit, and the collapsed trunks give off a sour, unpleasant smell as they lie rotting in the swamps. The sago of commerce, and the crude sago which is the basic food of some of the East Indies peoples, are made from the starchy pith of these palms. The ivory-nut palm of the Solomons is similar in appearance, but has a larger fruit and a very hard seed which is used for the manufacture of buttons.

STRENGTH OF WOOD

Strength Properties

The strength of wood is not a single property. There are several properties, each one of which expresses the strength of wood in resistance to a particular type of stress. The relation between these strength properties and certain influencing factors, such as specific gravity, has been fairly well established in a general way for American woods. Tropical woods have not been as fully investigated as temperate woods.

Recent investigations have shown, however, that the degree of lignification of the wood cells bears an important relation to strength properties, and tropical growth conditions intensify this process. When specific gravity is taken into account, there are no outstandingly tough tropical woods. Toughness, which is measured by impact bending, is a dual property. It is a combination of cross breaking strength and elasticity. Tropical woods are generally weaker in impact bending *but* stronger under compression parallel to the grain than temperate woods of the same specific gravity. The higher degree of lignification of the cell walls of tropical woods may result in this higher compressive strength but lower toughness. These relationships should be kept in mind when judging the value of tropical woods for specific construction purposes in the field.

Standard Strength Equations

The loads which members will support may be computed by transposition of and substitution into the following standard equations:

Static Bending.

13

1. Fiber stress at elastic limit

$$r = \frac{1.5\,P_1\,L}{bh^2}$$

2. Modulus of rupture

$$R = \frac{1.5\,P\,L}{bh^2}$$

3. Modulus of elasticity

$$E = \frac{P_1\,L^3}{4\,D\,bh^3}$$

Compression Parallel to the Grain.

1. Stress at elastic limit

$$c = \frac{P_1}{A}$$

2. Maximum crushing strength

$$C = \frac{P}{A}$$

Compression Perpendicular to the Grain.

1. Stress at elastic limit

$$c = \frac{P_1}{B}$$

Hardness.

No equation.

Legend.

P_1 = load at elastic limit in pounds ("safe load").

P = maximum load the piece will support in pounds.

L = length between supports in inches.

b = width of the base of the piece in inches.

h = height of the piece in inches.

A = area of the cross-section of the piece in

square inches.

$B =$ area of the portion of the piece which is under compression, in square inches.

Strength Data

Considerable testing of mechanical properties has been conducted on Philippine woods. Table 2 presents the results of tests on small clear specimens (2 x 2-in. cross-section) of wood in the green condition. Table 3 presents the results of tests on small clear specimens of wood in the air-dry (13–18 percent moisture) condition. Table 4 presents the results of tests of static bending on wood in structural sizes in the green condition. Table 5 presents the results of tests of static bending on wood in structural sizes in the air-dry condition. These tables show the results of tests on Philippine woods but since many of the genera included and several of the species also occur in the region covered by this manual, it is assumed that the results shown here are at least indications of the strength values which may be expected in the woods of the same genera or species in this region. It must be remembered, however, that these figures are *averages* of series of tests and are only *indicative* of the strength of specific individual pieces. Also, site (environment, including climate, soil, topography, and associated plants and animals) has a definite effect on wood quality. Any strength data must be accepted and used with the understanding that they are merely averages of series of tests on wood from a certain locality or localities, and adequate allowance must be left for this in any computation of working stresses.

15

TABLE 1.—Strength Values of Green Woods; Small Clear Specimens*

Scientific name	Common name (Philippines)	Number of tests	Moisture Content	Specific gravity At test	Specific gravity Oven-dry, based on volume at test	Static bending Fiber stress at elastic limit	Static bending Modulus of rupture	Static bending Modulus of elasticity	Compression parallel to grain Crushing strength at elastic limit	Compression parallel to grain Maximum crushing strength	Comp. perp. to grain; crushing strength at elastic limit	Shear parallel to grain	Hardness End	Hardness Side
			Per cent			Lb. per sq. in.	Lb. per sq. in.	1,000 lb. per sq. in.	Lb. per sq. in.	Lb. per sq. in.	Lb. per sq. in.	Lb. per sq. in.	Lb.	Lb.
Albizzia acle	Akle	20	96	1.01	0.53	5,447	8,520	1,052	3,200	4,310	1,358	1,153	6,656	7,154
Anisoptera thurifera	Palosapis	12	74	0.90	.50	5,035	8,235	1,493	3,598	3,897	711	1,065	714	723
Dipterocarpus grandiflorus	Apitong	16	39	.78	.58	5,035	9,401	1,934	3,271	4,480	683	1,135	5,618	5,049
Hopea acuminata	Manggach-apui	20	40	.88	.62	9,757	15,645	2,133	7,439	8,008	1,269	1,522	1,347	1,243
Hopea basilanica	Yakal	40	35	1.09	.86	11,137	17,921	2,532	6,045	8,207	1,877	1,821	1,823	1,958
Intsia bijuga	Ipil	32	46	1.10	.75	10,098	14,934	2,034	7,325	8,335	1,565	1,693	9,615	10,753
Koordersiodendron pinnatum	Amugis	20	43	1.04	.73	6,983	11,620	1,664	4,608	6,941	1,358	1,536	7,538	9,643
Mangifera altissima	Pahutan	8	38	.87	.70	7,140	12,744	1,835	4,267	5,789	1,064	1,437	1,085	1,052
Mimosops parvifolia	Bansalagin	16	39	1.06	.76	8,278	13,768	1,849	5,319	6,628	1,621	1,636	11,620	11,578
Neonauclea calycina	Kalaman-sanai	12	36	.93	.69	8,633	13,768	1,835	5,163	6,400	1,565	1,536	10,127	9,330
Pahudia rhomboidea	Tindalo	16	50	1.14	.77	7,709	12,175	1,593	4,878	6,443	1,721	1,693	10,354	11,080

15a

TABLE 1 (Cont.)

Scientific name	Common name (Philippines)	Number of tests	Moisture Content	Specific gravity — At test	Specific gravity — Oven-dry based on vol. at test	Static bending — Fiber stress at elastic limit	Static bending — Modulus of rupture	Static bending — Modulus of elasticity	Compression parallel to grain — Crushing strength at elastic limit	Compression parallel to grain — Maximum crushing strength	Comp. perp. to grain; crushing strength at elastic limit	Shear parallel to grain	Hardness; load required to embed a 1.12-cm ball half its diameter — End	Hardness — Side
			Per cent			Lb. per sq. in.	Lb. per sq. in.	1,000 lb. per sq. in.	Lb. per sq. in.	Lb. per sq. in.	Lb. per sq. in.	Lb. per sq. in.	Lb.	Lb.
Pinus insularis	Benguet pine	32	25	.74	.59	4,267	7,723	1,309	3,200	3,926	515	923	3,954	3,926
Planchonia spectabilis	Lamog	20	43	1.03	.71	5,646	9,373	1,280	3,044	4,679	1,334	1,451	1,541	1,647
Pometia pinnata	Malugay	32	47	.84	.57	5,490	10,041	1,451	3,641	4,381	816	1,186	996	999
Pterocarpus indicus	Narra	32	58	.82	.52	6,983	11,037	1,437	4,580	5,504	969	1,279	1,160	1,118
Shorea guiso	Gujo	12	35	.90	.70	8,150	14,650	1,963	5,632	6,599	1,172	1,493	1,290	1,398
Shorea negrosensis	Red lauan	120	48	.60	.40	4,665	7,339	1,280	2,802	3,684	485	449	481	514
Shorea palosapis	Mayapis	8	38	.46	.38	4,253	6,742	1,237	2,190	3,257	367	663	441	399
Shorea polysperma	Tangile	52	37	.69	.53	4,167	8,591	1,479	2,916	4,238	600	1,006	666	679
Sindora supa	Supa	12	34	.73	.55	5,604	9,529	1,408	3,271	4,566	1,206	1,344	7,638	5,263
Sonneratia caseolaris	Pagatpat	20	63	1.03	.63	7,140	10,610	1,522	4,750	5,618	1,185	1,321	8,249	7,382
Tarrietia javanica	Lumbayao	12	37	.70	.56	4,352	8,648	1,365	3,172	4,423	767	1,028	4,452	4,182
Tarrietia sylvatica	Dungon	16	45	1.13	.77	6,201	10,710	1,365	3,399	5,021	1,367	1,465	10,909	12,317
Vatica mangachapoi	Narig	8	44	1.09	.75	11,009	13,725	2,304	5,888	7,538	1,650	1,678	1,704	1,667
Vitex pauiflora	Molave	16	40	.99	.71	8,192	13,327	1,863	6,116	7,097	1,422	1,451	1,281	1,380
Wallaceodendron celebicum	Banuya	16	60	.95	.60	6,784	10,781	1,721	4,310	4,978	855	1,286	6,329	6,343

*Source: Espinosa, J. C., "Comparative Strength Properties of the Principal Philippine Commercial Woods." *Philippine Journal of Science*, Vol. 33, May–August, pp. 381–394, 1927. (Revised to meet the needs of this manual.)

TABLE 2.—*Strength Values of Air-dry Woods; Small Clear Specimens**

Scientific name	Common name (Philippines)	Number of tests	Moisture Content	Specific gravity — At test	Specific gravity — Oven-dry, based on volume	Static bending — Fiber stress at elastic limit	Static bending — Modulus of rupture	Static bending — Modulus of elasticity	Compression parallel to grain — Crushing strength at elastic limit	Compression parallel to grain — Maximum crushing strength	Comp. perp. to grain; crushing strength at elastic limit	Shear parallel to grain	Hardness; load required to embed a 1.12-cm ball half its diameter — End	Hardness — Side
			Per cent			*Lb. per sq. in.*	*Lb. per sq. in.*	*1,000 lb. per sq. in.*	*Lb. per sq. in.*	*Lb. per sq. in.*	*Lb. per sq. in.*	*Lb. per sq. in.*	*Lb.*	*Lb.*
Anisoptera thurifera	Palosapis	104	15	0.64	0.54	5,376	10,184	1,550	3,783	4,665	831	1,225	805	783
Dipterocarpus grandiflorus	Apitong	484	17	.71	.61	6,500	11,165	1,934	4,438	5,476	863.3	1,254.4	5,760	5,433
Homalium luzoiense	Aranga	72	13	.94	.83	9,842	15,219	2,261	6,03.	9,088	2,190	1,764	2,094	1,854
Hopea basilanica	Yakal	160	16	.95	.91	11,322	19,343	2,802	6,31	8,420	210	1,778	1,907	1,997
Mangifera altissima	Pahutan	36	18	.81	.65	6,159	11,649	1,949	4,856	6,116	1,070	1,508	1,316	1,140
Palaquium luzoniense	Nato	64	17	.69	.55	5,476	10,056	1,479	3,527	4,708	1,019.8	1,278.6	5,959	5,405
Parashorea plicata	Bagtikan	60	16	.65	.57	6,884	11,165	1,735	4,750	5,447	928.8	1,255.9	5,006	5,291
Pentacme contorta	White la-an	212	17	.59	.50	5,588	10,169	1,664	4,335	5,135	688.4	1,150.6	5,504	4,324
Shorea eximia	Almon	112	17	.59	.50	6,969	10,312	1,806	5,049	5,547	791	1,129	650	719
Shorea guiso	Guijo	192	16	.86	.73	8,776	14,223	2,261	5,817	7,424	1,493	1,621	1,188	1,312
Shorea negrosensis	Red lauan	248	17	.60	.51	5,974	9,657	1,593	4,310	5,206	750	1,148	650	633
Shorea polysperma	Tangile	388	16	.61	.55	5,830	10,169	1,650	3,923	5,021	764	1,077	666	655
Shorea sp.	Ma-igga-sinoro	76	15	.51	.44	5,106	8,249	1,380	3,395	4,466	671.3	1,109.4	4.95	3,968
Tarrietia javanica	Lumbayao	128	17	.64	.53	5,575	10,667	1,593	3,883	5,604	881.8	1,241.7	5,30	4,708

*Source: Espinosa, J. C., "Comparative Strength Properties of the Principal Philippine Commercial Woods." *Philippine Journal of Science*, Vol. 33, May–August, pp. 381 394, 1927. (Revised to meet the needs of this manual.)

15c

TABLE 3.—*Strength Values in Static Bending of Green Woods; Structural Sizes from 2 Inches by 4 Inches by 6 Feet to 8 Inches by 8 Inches by 12 Feet**

Scientific name	Common name (Philippines)	Number of tests	Moisture content	Specific gravity — At test	Specific gravity — Oven-dry, based on volume at test	Static bending — Fiber stress at elastic limit	Static bending — Modulus of rupture	Static bending — Modulus of elasticity
			Percent			*Lbs. per sq. in.*	*Lbs. per sq. in.*	*1,000 lbs. per sq. in.*
Albizzia acle	Akle	9	79	1.10	0.56	4,182	5,931	1,095
Anisoptera thurifera	Palosapis	16	61	0.86	.54	4,537	7,908	1,550
Dipterocarpus grandiflora	Apitong	14	40	.82	.60	4,807	7,097	1,636
Dracontomelum dao	Dao	4	42	.84	.59	5,334	8,875	1,678
Eucalyptus deglupta	Amamanit	5	52	.86	.58	4,722	7,894	1,821
Hopea acuminata	Manggachapui	10	38	.73	.53	8,235	10,994	2,318
Hopea basilanica	Yakal	31	36	1.17	.86	8,008	13,000	2,318
Homalium luzoicnse	Aranga	6	31	.99	.76	5,291	7,282	1,806
Intsia bijuga	Ipil	8	49	1.14	.78	8,463	11,236	2,261
Kingiodendron alternaefolium	Batete	10	52	.76	.50	5,277	8,392	1,821
Koordersiodendron pinnatum	Amugis	10	46	1.03	.71	6,358	10,212	1,636
Mimusops parvifolia	Bansalagin	4	40	1.03	.77	6,827	10,881	1,792
Neonauclea calycina	Kalamansani	9	43	.81	.54	6,230	10,241	2,020
Pahudia rhomboidea	Tindalo	7	50	1.09	.71	6,912	10,411	1,636
Pentacme contorta	White lauan	5	45	.65	.41	3,428	6,130	1,237
Pinus insularis	Benguet pine	8	35	.65	.49	3,670	5,519	1,437

15d

TABLE 3. (Cont.)

Scientific name	Common name (Philippines)	Number of tests	Moisture content	Specific gravity		Static bending		
				At test	Oven-dry, based on volume at test	Fiber stress at elastic limit	Modulus of rupture	Modulus of elasticity
			Per cent			Lbs. per sq. in.	Lbs. per sq. in.	1,000 lbs. per sq. in.
Planchonia spectabilis	Lamog	8	46	1.04	.71	5,476	8,448	1,195
Pometia pinnata	Malugay	8	51	.66	.44	5,220	7,538	1,565
Pterocarpus indicus	Narra	7	71	.95	.56	4,907	7,680	1,408
Sindora supa	Supa	5	34	.92	.69	4,466	6,898	1,536
Sonneratia caseolaris	Pagatpat	10	53	.89	.57	5,632	8,818	1,237
Shorea guiso	Guijo	7	38	.92	.67	7,624	11,051	2,247
Shorea negrosensis	Red lauan	31	58	.62	.39	3,769	6,130	1,380
Shorea palosapis	Mayapis	5	34	.45	.34	2,702	5,049	1,223
Shorea polysperma	Tangile	27	37	.69	.50	4,992	7,894	1,735
Shorea sp.	Manggasinoro	6	36	.59	.44	2,660	5,647	1,152
Tarrietia javanica	Lumbayao	8	35	.65	.48	4,637	7,183	1,508
Tarrietia sylvatica	Dungon	7	47	1.18	.84	4,935	9,245	1,508
Vatica mangachapoi	Narig	3	49	1.11	.73	8,079	11,762	2,361
Vitex parviflora	Molave	3	45	.92	.63	7,951	10,994	2,034
Wallaceodendron celebicum	Banuyo	4	61	.84	.52	5,462	8,192	1,835

15e

"Source: Espinosa, J. C., "Comparative Strength Properties of the Principal Philippine Commercial Woods." *Philippine Journal of Science*, Vol. 33, May-August, pp. 381-394, 1927. (Revised to meet the needs of this manual).

TABLE 4.—Strength Values in Static Bending of Air-dry Woods; Structural Sizes from 2 Inches by 4 Inches by 6 Feet to 8 Inches by 8 Inches by 12 Feet*

Scientific name	Common name (Philippines)	Number of tests	Moisture content	Specific gravity		Static bending		
				At test	Oven-dry, based on volume at test	Fiber stress at elastic limit	Modulus of rupture	Modulus of elasticity
			Per cent			Lbs. per sq. in.	Lbs. per sq. in.	1,000 lbs. per sq. in.
Anisoptera thurifera	Palosapis	60	14	0.63	0.55	4,281	8,406	1,465
Dipterocarpus grandiflorus	Apitong	202	16	.72	.62	5,177	9,202	1,806
Homalium luzoniense	Aranga	45	16	.92	.79	6,471	10,237	1,991
Hopea basilanica	Yakal	78	20	1.03	.86	7,894	14,365	2,432
Mangifera altissima	Pahutan	40	12	.60	.54	3,513	5,632	1,451
Palaquium luzoniense	Nato	54	15	.68	.59	3,826	6,358	1,389
Parashorea plicata	Bagtikan	90	15	.62	.54	5,063	8,804	1,522
Pentacme contorta	White lauan	134	15	.58	.50	4,665	7,752	1,522
Sindora supa	Supa	24	14	.78	.68	5,945	12,573	1,778
Shorea eximia	Almon	222	14	.55	.49	4,637	8,701	1,593
Shorea guiso	Guijo	108	17	.89	.76	6,685	13,156	1,465
Shorea negrosensis	Red lauan	130	18	.60	.51	5,021	8,278	1,635
Shorea polysperma	Tangile	271	16	.60	.52	4,793	8,776	1,607
Shorea sp.	Manggasinoro	62	15	.51	.44	3,485	6,742	1,181
Tarrietia javanica	Lumbayao	35	18	.61	.52	4,950	7,680	1,565

*Source: Espinosa, J. C., "Comparative Strength Properties of the Principal Philippine Commercial Woods." *Philippine Journal of Science*, Vol. 33, May–August, pp. 381–394, 1927. (Revised to meet the needs of this manual.)

15 *f*

DURABILITY OF WOOD

The principal destructive agents affecting wood are fungi and insects. The resistance of wood to these destructive agents is by no means uniform. It varies between species, between heartwood and sapwood of the same species, and with the conditions of temperature, moisture, and air supply under which the wood is used.

There have been no extensive tests of the durability of the woods of the region covered by this manual; for this reason, reliance must be placed on experience with some of the woods in use. The experience of natives will be very valuable in this problem and they should be fully consulted regarding their experience with woods to be used in construction or regarding what woods are considered durable in their locality. In general, the woods of the widely distributed families *Dipterocarpaceae* and *Rhizophoraceae* are highly durable, some even when in contact with salt water.

While many of the woods of the region are durable in contact with the soil, very few are resistant to the attacks of marine borers. The woods which are fairly resistant are often not readily obtainable in sizes and quantities sufficiently large for large dock construction. The general practice has been to use less dense woods which may be more easily impregnated with a chemical preservative and which may be readily obtained in the large sizes required.

Protection From Fungi

The high temperature and humidity of the region are particularly favorable to the growth of fungi. Infection is accomplished by minute air-borne spores and by fungal hyphae from the soil, and it is spread throughout the wood by the hyphae. The presence and development of rot in wood is not apparent until an advanced stage is reached and the piece is almost completely destroyed or is so weakened that it breaks. For this reason, it is particularly important to exercise as much precaution as possible in the construction of even the most temporary type, to prevent or at least retard the development of fungi in the wood.

Wood not treated with a preservative should not be placed in construction work any closer than 2 ft. from the ground. At points of excessive moisture in the building, the source should be stopped if possible, or metal sheathing installed between the moisture source and the wood, and the accumulated water conducted outside to the ground without contact with the wood of the building. All wooden buildings should have ample ventilation beneath them. All underbrush and debris should be removed from beneath and immediately around the structure at the time of construction and not allowed to accumulate again. If the building has a double-wall construction, ample air drainage should be provided between the walls; this same precaution holds for floors. Adequate soil drainage should be provided to conduct all rain water away from the building. Wood used in the construction of structures of all types should be carefully examined before it is used to attempt to discover the presence of decay. Any

18

piece with even a small decayed portion should not be used, for, under the climatic conditions of the region, it will probably continue to develop and cause trouble later on. Only dry wood should be used in construction. Of course, it is realized that much of the construction in advance bases will be so urgent as to preclude the possibility of obtaining even partially seasoned lumber; but whenever dried lumber is available no unseasoned material should be used. Wet wood is not only susceptible to infection by fungi but is liable to shrink, crack, warp, or twist as it dries in place in the structure.

Protection From Insects

The most destructive insect in buildings is the termite. Only hard metals, solid rock, brick, and concrete are free from attack. However, even brick and mortar construction may be penetrated through small cracks and crevices. There are two general types of termites, the *subterranean termites* which must come from the soil and maintain contact with it, and the *dry wood termites* which do not require a moisture supply and contact with the soil. The former are more common and more destructive, but it is more difficult to protect buildings from the latter, especially in temporary construction under field conditions.

Since subterranean termites must maintain contact with the soil, permanent protection can be secured with complete separation of all woodwork from the ground for a distance of at least two feet. The above suggestions for minimizing damage from wood-rotting fungi also hold for protection from subterranean termites. Building for permanent or semipermanent use should have metal or concrete foundation corner posts topped with sheet metal shields which project out from the posts for several inches and are beveled downward at an angle of about 45°. Small, light, temporary buildings could probably be based on rows of metal oil drums set on end which would give certain protection. It must be remembered, however, that the subterranean termites can pass over resistant materials by the use of constructed enclosed passageways on the surface of the material and a constant watch for these must be kept. They may even build unsupported tubes up from the ground, but if all wood is kept at a distance of at least 2 ft. away, the danger from this source is not great. All pipes or other connections from the buildings to the ground should be fitted with downward-sloped metal shields and inspected frequently.

If posts are footed in a concrete base, a small channel in the top of the concrete post surrounding the wooden one should be kept filled with preservative. In buildings in which an attack is in progress, all affected material should be removed as soon as possible.

Preservative Treatment

While there are some exceptions, the generalization may be made that the darker, heavier woods are more resistant to both insects and fungi and the lighter-colored, less dense woods are more susceptible. Within species, the heartwood is generally more durable than the sapwood because of repellent or toxic substances deposited in the wood cells.

If it is possible to obtain and apply, a preservative should be applied to all wood used in construction at or near the ground or around water (especially salt water). The most generally effective wood preservative is coal tar creosote. It gives good protection against both fungi and insects and is fairly easy to apply. Application may be by brush or with a cloth dauber on a short pole. The butts of poles or posts may be treated by placing them in an open 100-gal. oil drum over a source of heat and raising the temperature of the creosote to about 220°F for from 1 to 12 hours depending on the species of wood, its condition and the depth of penetration desired. The source of heat is then removed and the poles allowed to stand in the creosote until it cools, or they may be removed.and placed in an adjacent drum of cool creosote for from 1 to 6 hours.

The wood should be dried before the application of any preservative; this is particularly important in the brush and dauber application methods. Effective penetration cannot be obtained in wet wood.

Regarding the protection of salt water piling and other structural members from the various marine borers, little can be done. Very few woods are naturally resistant, but whenever these are available, they should be used as much as possible. Non-resistant woods may be made more resistant by treatment, by the open-tank method, with hot creosote; but any attempt at mechanical protection by sheathing with metal sheets or by other methods will be found to be more bother than it is worth in protection.

In the section of this manual dealing with the descriptions of individual trees, information was included on the durability of the wood whenever it was available.

DESCRIPTION OF THE TREES
AND THEIR WOODS

Taxaceae

(Yew Family)

Small to large resinous trees, with fissured and spreading or drooping branches; leaves thin, long-pointed, abruptly contracted at the base, dark green, lustrous, and slightly rounded above; flowers axillary and solitary; fruit a hard, bony shell, containing a single seed. The family has ten genera widely distributed over the world.

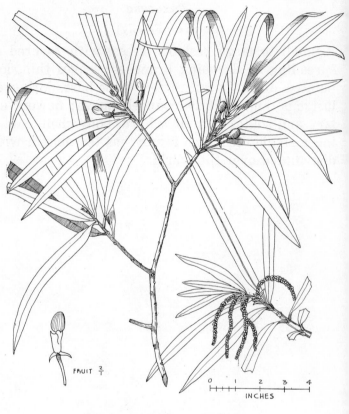

FRUIT $\frac{2}{1}$

0 1 2 3 4
INCHES

FIGURE 1. *Podocarpus neriifolia*

Podocarpus neriifolia (Fig. 1)

Local Names. Thitminpo (Burma); sentada, tadji, tjeban, jati bukit (Malay Peninsula); sitoboe hotang (North Sumatra, Battak country); naroe dotan (Simaloe Is., off N.W. Sumatra); handalaksa, ki bima, ki maleta, ki pantjar, ki poetri, ki sireum (Sunda Is.); tadju, woeloean (Java); bankol (Madur).

Habit. Attains 75 ft. in height, with whorled branches.

Leaves. Narrow lanceolate, 2 to 5 in. long, thick and stiff, with prominent midrib, scattered or in whorls of 3 to 5.

Flowers. Borne solitary on peduncles about ⅛ in. long, fleshy, yellowish-green, changing to orange-red, then to purple.

Fruit. The base of the fruit is fleshy and enlarged, bearing the round, seed-bearing nut; seeds are ovoid, smooth, green, about ⅛ in. in diameter.

Bark. Gray, thin, and fibrous.

Wood. Buff color; medium hard; texture fine; grain straight or crossed; weight about 42 lb. per cu. ft.; growth rings generally indistinct, marked by the narrow, dense, late wood; parenchyma diffuse, filled with reddish or whitish deposits; rays very narrow, indistinct, few in number; works easily and seasons well; considered generally durable even when exposed or in contact with the ground; suitable for boat construction, building construction, carving, flooring, and boxes.

Occurrence. Burma, Malay Peninsula, Southern China, French Indo-China, and East Indies generally.

Pinaceae

(Pine Family)

Trees and evergreen shrubs chiefly of the north temperate and torrid zones, distinguished by presence of resin in all parts of the plants; leaves needle-shaped, except in *Agathis*, entire and parallel-veined; fruit, a woody cone: timber very valuable.

Agathis alba

Local Names.—Beboeloe-s, hamar pilau, damar minjak, pohon iamar (Malayan); kajoe solo (N. Celebes); ajoedamahoe (Gorontalo); gongodomagoe (Boelo); ongkoa, soga (Baree); ise, kama-l (Ambon); kajoe damara (Makassar); kolano (N. Halmahera); hate salo boboedo (Ternate); Philippines: aninga, aningat (Ilocos region, Cagayan, Mountain provinces); saleng (Cagayan, Isabela); titan (Abra); anteng (Nueva Ecija); uli (Zambales); adiangau, dadiangau or ladiangau (Tayabas, Camarines Norte, Camarines Sur, Albay, Sorsagan); badiangau (Negros); bagtik (Palawan); makan (Misamis); hahos (Davao).

Habit.—A large tree reaching 150 in. in diameter and 180 ft. in height with 60 to 90 ft. of clear length. The trunk is straight and cylindrical.

Leaves.—Simple, opposite or alternate, broad, leathery.

Flowers.—Small, borne in clusters.

Fruit.—Cones ovate, globular, with persistent scales.

Bark.—Dark brown, rough, dull, slightly checkered.

Wood.—Sapwood not sharply demarcated from the pinkish-brown heartwood; growth rings not distinct, marked by dense wood; rays very narrow, few in number, straight; parenchyma scattered or diffuse; specific gravity, air-dry, 0.389 to 0.630, average 0.527; straight-grained, fine texture, glossy, without pronounced odor or taste; light to comparatively heavy, soft to moderately hard, moderately strong, seasons well, very easy to work. It is subject to attack by termites when used for interior work and is not durable when exposed to the weather or in contact with the ground. Has been used for making scale rules, engineering instruments and household utensils. In New Zealand and Australia a very' similar wood, the Kauri pine (*Agathis Australis*), is used for nearly all types of general construction and for engineering pattern work.

Occurrence.—Philippines. Found in most islands and provinces from Balwyanes to Palawan and Mindanao at medium and high altitudes; occasionally found at sea level at a few places, such as on the Caramoan Peninsula in southern Luzon.

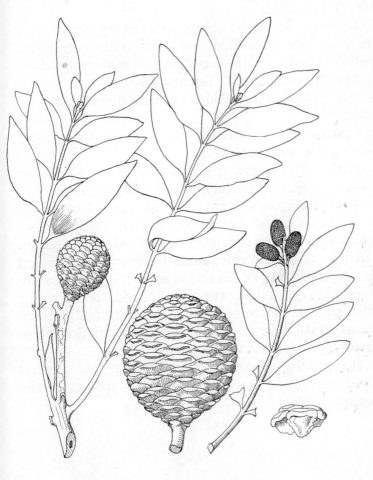

FIGURE 2.—*Agathis labillardieri*

29

Agathis labillardieri (Fig. 2)

Local Names.—Waigui (Dutch New Guinea) ; damma (Regimal, New Guinea).

Habit.—A large tree 3 to 4 ft. in diameter and 100 ft. in height.

Leaves.—Scattered or opposite; evergreen; 1 to 2 in. long and about half as wide, with very short petioles; leathery; have resinous odor when crushed.

Flowers—Male and female flowers on separate trees; male flowers catkins; female flowers globular cones.

Fruit.—Solitary globose cone with one two-winged seed under each scale.

Bark.—Thick, fibrous and drops thin shreds; inner bark exudes nearly odorless and tasteless resin.

Wood.—Sapwood thin, not sharply demarcated from pale yellow heartwood, which turns darker when seasoned; rays numerous and indistinct; parenchyma scattered throughout the growth rings and in a terminal line at the end of each ring; moderately hard, heavy, tough, straight-grained, texture fine and smooth, seasons well and works easily, very durable; suitable for all ordinary construction, shipbuilding, furniture making, etc.

Occurrence.—New Guinea, Philippines. Several other species in the genus are also present in the region.

Araucaria cunninghamii

Local Names.—Yau (Kemp Welsh people; also on the hills along the Ramu River).

Habit.—A large tree, to 5 ft. in diameter and 150 ft. in height with a clear length of 80 ft.

Leaves.—Stiff and slender.

Fruit.—A cone.

Bark.—¾ to 1 in. thick, dark, very scaly, peels off horizontally in thick papery layers; inner bark mottled brown and white; exudes a white opaque resin.

Wood.—Streaked with white and yellow; rays 200 per in., indistinct but appear dark yellow on radial surface; specific gravity about 0.560; should be a good general purpose wood; it is one of the most important softwoods of Australia.

Occurrence.—New Guinea. Occurs in same general regions and localities as *A. klinkii* but does not intermingle with it. Lower elevation of main belt at about 4,000 ft., on Mount Obree; common along ranges on both sides of Ramu-Markham Valley from 1,500 to 4,000 ft.

FIGURE 3.—*Araucaria klinkii.*

Araucaria klinkii (Fig. 3)

Local Names.—Pai (Waria), rassu (Ongoruna).

Habit.—A large tree, to 3 ft. in diameter and 150 ft. in height; branches in whorls.

Leaves.—Very stiff and borne at ends of branches.

Bark.—1¼ in. thick, dark reddish-brown; inner bark rich red on outer side but fades to pink toward inside; exudes a colorless resin.

Wood.—Yellow in color; chops easily; frequent resin deposits; rays indistinct, coarse, about 90 per in., appear as dark yellow oblongs on radial surface; fine grain and compact; pale yellow color has alternating rings of slightly darker yellow; specific gravity about 0.610; should be a good general purpose wood; was logged and milled in goldfields area behind Huon Gulf.

Occurrence.—New Guinea. Occurs in same general regions and localities as *A. cunninghamii* but does not intermingle with it. Common between 2,000 and 6,000 ft. behind Finschhafen and on the hills of the upper Ramu River; Waria and goldfields behind the Huon Gulf.

Gnetaceae

(Joint Fir Family)

103. Mostly small trees or creeping shrubs with jointed stems and branches, and opposite, netted-veined, sometimes scaly leaves. Native of temperate as well as warm regions of Europe, Asia, and South America. Seeds of some species are roasted and eaten.

Gnetum gnemon

Local Names.—Suffitz (Yalu, Lower Markham Valley), genda (Buna), doro (Vailala and Kérema), malindjo (Malayan); wahoe, bangoe, soeka (N. Celebes); bohoe (Gorontalo); bogoe (Boelo); saeka (Baree); oesa (Moena); bagoe, poko soemba (Makassar); soswa (Boegina); hoek (Kai I.); tjamale, oewa, sowa-lo (W. and S. Ceram); soewa-l (Ambon, Oeliaser); oetramal (Boeroe); Loi, roeki-ti, bisia (Halmahera).

Habit.—Attains 2 ft. in diameter and 60 ft. in height; without buttresses.

Leaves.—Simple opposite; petiole ½ in. long; blade 1 to 2 in. by 5 to 9, elliptical or lanceolate, thin, smooth; young leaves edible.

Flowers.—Borne in axillary spikes, 2½ in. long.

Fruit.—Purple when ripe, ellipsoid, 1½ in. by ½ in.; kernel is edible.

Bark.—Smooth, gray; with raised rings about 1 ft. apart along trunk; used to make rough cordage.

Wood.—Yellowish, coarse-grained, easy to split, fairly oily, moderately hard and heavy; used as a green fuel for cooking fires; durable in fresh water; used for river piling.

Occurrence.—New Guinea, probably also in Bismarcks and Solomons; on coastal plains up to 2,000 ft. in foothills.

Casuarinaceae

(Beefwood Family)

Trees and shrubs naturally confined to Australia, New Caledonia, New Guinea, and Indian Archipelago, but now widely planted for shade and ornament throughout the tropical and sub-tropical world. A group of about 20 species of jointed leafless trees with slender, green, jointed branchlets, conspicuous because of their remote resemblance to the pines; bark rich in tannin and dyeing substances; wood is hard, often called beefwood.

FIGURE 4. *Casuarina equisetifolia*

Casuariana equisetifolia (Fig. 4)

Local Names. Oak, she-oak, filao de l'Inde, beef-wood, polynesian ironwood, (Trade); aru, eru, ru, eroe, tjemara, chemara laut (Malay Peninsula); aroen, oroe, emboen, haroe (Sumatra); naroeoe (Nias Is. off N. W. Sumatra); kajoe embon, araoe, kajoe walaoe, montaga (Borneo); tjamara (Sunda Is., Java, Madura); kajoe merak, tjemara (Bali); kejoe (Sumba).

Habit. Attains 3 ft. in diameter and 100 ft. in height.

Leaves. Very small, whorled scales on slender, jointed, green branchlets; these branchlets also function as leaves.

Fruit. Cone-like and composed of woody bracts enclosing the winged seeds.

Bark. Gray, coarse, scales flake off.

Wood. Sapwood pale brown, not sharply demarcated from the brown heartwood; rays broad to quite fine; pores medium in size, in irregular radial rows, often filled with a yellow deposit; growth rings absent; hard and very heavy; specific gravity 0.704 to 0.942; texture fairly fine; difficult to work and to surface; splits easily; liable to split on drying; is used for fuel; used for piling in Australia but durability in this use is not known; suitable for general repair and small construction requiring a hard wood.

Occurrence. Beaches and low sandy river banks near coasts and occasionally inland in sandy river valleys.

Juglandaceae

(Walnut Family)

Large or sometimes shrubby trees, commonly strong-scented; leaves alternate, pinnately compound; flowers small, greenish, arranged in long drooping catkins; fruit a very hard nut, inclosed in a thick dry husk; seeds deeply lobed, usually edible. The species are usually widely distributed in the North Temperate Zone and in the high mountains of both hemispheres. The hickories *(Carya)* and walnuts *(Juglans)* are the principal representatives.

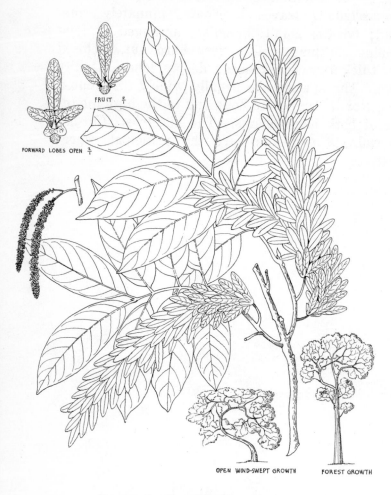

FRUIT $\frac{2}{1}$

FORWARD LOBES OPEN $\frac{2}{1}$

OPEN WIND-SWEPT GROWTH   FOREST GROWTH

FIGURE 5. *Engelhardtia spicata*

40

Engelhardtia spicata (Fig. 5)

Local Names. Ki hoedjan, ki keper (Sunda Is.); klimasawa, marasawa, mesaw (Java).

Habit. Attains about 65 ft. in height and 45 in. in diameter with a clear length of 30 to 45 ft.; trunk is cylindrical and without buttresses; young branchlets with soft, fine hairs.

Leaves. Pinnately compound, 4 to 6 pairs of leaflets which are ovate to lanceolate, 4 to 5 in. long, with smooth margins.

Flowers. Borne in loose panicles which are 6 to 8 in. long.

Fruit. A small globose nut subtended by a 3-lobed bract.

Bark. Contains tannin.

Wood. Sapwood light gray, not sharply demarcated from the grayish-brown heartwood; growth rings indistinct; vessels isolated and in groups, small to fairly large, few in number, some tyloses present; parenchyma in lines or bands, diffuse, fairly numerous; rays with dark brown deposits, few to numerous; cross-grained, fine-textured; glossy; soft to medium hard, light to heavy; specific gravity, air-dry, 0.510; moderately strong and tough; seasons well and is easy to work; durable in interior construction but not decay resistant in contact with the ground; suitable for general construction and cabinetmaking.

Occurrence: Found in forests at low and medium altitudes but is not abundant; Burma, French Indo-China, Malay Peninsula.

Fagaceae

(Beech Family)

Trees and shrubs widely distributed, chiefly throughout the northern hemisphere; leaves alternate, deciduous or persistent; bark thick and tannin-bearing; fruit a one-seeded nut; wood is valuable.

FRUIT

0 1 2 3 4
INCHES

FIGURE 7. *Castanopsis megacarpa*

FIGURE 6.—*Castanopsis junghuhnii.*

Castanopsis junghuhnii (Fig. 6)

Local Names.—Kini (Buna District).

Habit.—Resembles the oaks in general appearance and size.

Wood.—Yellow-brown; rays fine and numerous; pores in zones; parenchyma diffuse; growth rings firm and inconspicuous; crossed grain; fine texture; hard and heavy; a good strong general purpose repair wood.

Occurrence.—New Guinea; occurs with the oaks and also at lower elevations but above the low coastal areas.

Castanopsis megacarpa (C. javanica) (**Fig. 7**)

Local Names. Sebilek, kata bilek, berangan, berangen bukit, berangen duri, berangan gajah, keretak tangga (Malay Peninsula); kalimborot, ki hijoer, rijoeng (Sunda Is.).

Habit. Attains 80 ft. in height.

Leaves. Oblong, leathery, bright green above, reddish and with fine hairs below, blade 2 by 5 in. to 4½ by 6 in.; petioles ½ to 1 in. long.

Flowers. Borne in spikes which are 4 in. long.

Fruit. Globose, 3 in. long, outer coating thick and hard, with ½ in. spines; contains one nut or seed.

Bark. Thick, bears tannin.

Wood. Woods of the genus differ only in minor anatomical features. They are yellowish-brown, moderately hard and heavy, cross- or wavy-grained and fine-textured; without distinctive taste or odor; growth rings inconspicuous; pores ring-porous; parenchyma diffuse; rays narrow and numerous; easy to work and yields a smooth finish; considered fairly durable.

Occurrence. Common in lowland forests, Malay Peninsula, Java, Sumatra, Borneo; many other allied species throughout the region.

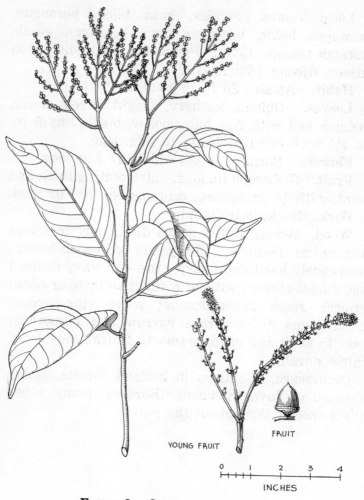

YOUNG FRUIT

FRUIT

0   1   2   3   4
INCHES

FIGURE 8. *Quercus bennettii*

Quercus bennettii (Fig. 8)

Local Names. Oak; pasang-pasang soeloh (S.E. Sumatra, Lampong).

Habit. Attains 40 in. in diameter and 100 ft. in height, with small buttresses.

Leaves. Simple, 4 to 5 in. long, broadly elliptical.

Flowers. Small, erect.

Fruit. An acorn, ¾ to 1 in. in diameter.

Wood. Sapwood not sharply demarcated from the tan heartwood; growth rings indistinct; pores arranged in oblique chains, few in number, small to fairly large; parenchyma surrounding the pores and in concentric lines, narrow and numerous; rays narrow and broad, few in number; straight-grained, coarse-textured, dull in appearance; without characteristic taste or odor; very heavy, hard, and strong; specific gravity, air-dry, 1.027 to 1.104, average 1.056; seasons well if carefully piled; is difficult to work; very durable in interior use but only moderately durable when exposed or in contact with the ground; has been used for general house construction and some for furniture and interior finish.

Occurrence. Malay Peninsula, Java, Borneo; many allied species throughout the region.

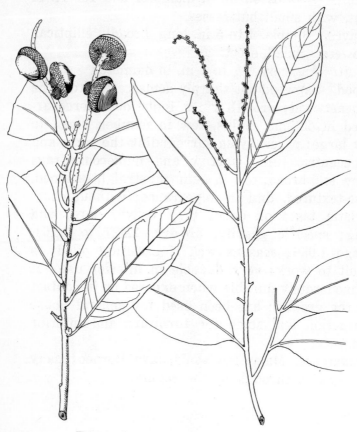

FIGURE 9. –*Quercus psuedo-molucca.*

Quercus pseudo-molucca (Fig. 9)

Local Names.—Oak, hobaba (Buna), hopapa (Embi), koroba (Suku).

Habit.—A large tree, to 3½ ft. in diameter and 100 ft. in height with 80 ft. of clear length; without buttresses.

Leaves.—Simple, alternate; petiole ¼ in. long; blade 1 to 2 in. by 3 to 6 in., margins entire but wavy, lanceolate or oblanceolate, pale yellow, with whitish bloom below.

Fruit.—An acorn.

Bark.—Gray; inner bark red-brown.

Wood.—Yellow to brown; sapwood not demarcated from heartwood; rays conspicuous, both coarse and fine; pores conspicuous, 1,500 to 3,000 per sq. in., in sinuous radial chains; parenchyma in fine lines at right angles to rays, 160 per in.; broad silver grain or radial surface; specific gravity 0.754 to 0.818; cuts hard; a good general purpose wood with typical oak properties.

Occurrence.—New Guinea, above 1,000 ft. elevation; one of several species in this genus.

FIGURE 10. *Quercus soleriana*

Quercus soleriana (Fig. 10)

Local Names.—Oak, katabang, manaring (Philippines).

Habit.—Attains 40 in. in diameter and considerable height; the habit varies widely with sites, from small shrubby form on poor sites to large size with long clear length on the better sites.

Leaves.—Alternate, entire and leathery; 5 to 6 in. long; dark green and glossy above and slightly pubescent below; similar to leaves of the evergreen (live) oaks of the Western Hemisphere.

Flowers.—Both male and female flowers borne on same tree; male flower a catkin; female flowers surrounded by scales.

Fruit.—A hard nut enclosed in a scaly cup, an acorn.

Bark.—About 1 in. thick, from light to dark grayish-brown, wide ridges and shallow, narrow furrows, hard, coarse and brittle; inner bark reddish; contains abundant tannin.

Wood.—Sapwood thin, white and not sharply demarcated from the slightly darker heartwood; rays both wide and narrow, very numerous, equidistantly spaced; pores fairly large, easily visible, arranged in distinct radial rows between the rays; parenchyma about the pores and in numerous narrow concentric lines; growth rings indistinct, hard, moderately heavy, is liable to some warping and checking in seasoning; has been used to some extent for construction timbers, posts, flooring and railroad ties in the Philippines.

Occurrence.—Generally distributed throughout the Philippines; common on exposed ridges and in the Mossy Forest above 3,600 ft. elevation; other species in this genus are present throughout the region.

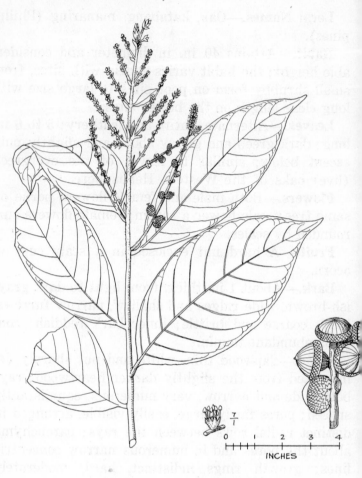

FIGURE 11. *Quercus sundaica*

Quercus sundaica (Pasania sundaica) (Fig. 11)

Local Names. Oak; mempening bagan, bintangor tuba (Malay Peninsula); sela-sela (Simaloe I., off N.W. Sumatra); pasang batoe, pasang parengpeng, paseng soengsoean (Sunda Is.); pasang baloeng, pasang djambeh, pasang kapoer, wrakas (Java); kasang (Madura).

Habit. Attains 60 to 80 ft. in height; with furry or fuzzy branches

Leaves. Simple, leathery, ovate or elliptical, 2 by 4 in. to 3 by 7 in., smooth on upper surface, lighter and with fine fuzz on lower surface; petiole about ¼ in. long.

Flowers. Small, erect, slender, numerous, borne in terminal panicles which are 4 to 8 in. long.

Fruit. An acorn, about ½ in. in diameter and 1 in. long.

Wood. Similar to that of *Quercus bennettii*.

Occurrence. Common; Malay Peninsula, Java, Sumatra, Borneo.

Ulmaceae

(Elm Family)

This is a small family of about 15 genera. The leaves are alternate and simple. The flowers are clustered or solitary on the current or previous season's growth. *Ulmus,* in which genus the American elm is contained, is the best known.

FIGURE 12. *Celtis philippensis*

Celtis philippensis (Fig. 12)

Local Names.—Hanuma (Buna), gotgot (New Britain), mougong (Lower Markham Valley), wai-am-a-hasi (Suku), ha-adi (Vailala); kajoe sirih (Malayan, Moluccas); sessel (Ambon); ai salo (Boeroe).

Habit.—Attains 2½ ft. in diameter and 120 ft. in height with 70 ft. of clear length; with buttresses.

Leaves.—Simple, alternate; petiole ½ in. long; veination palmate; smooth above, with fine hairs below; blade 4 to 8 in. by 2 to 5 in.; leaves fall in June but only bare for 2 or 3 days.

Flowers.—Borne in axillary panicles.

Fruit.—A drupe, globose, ¾ in. in diameter; red and green when ripe; contains hard "nut", ⅜ in. in diameter, with a white kernel.

Bark.—Greenish-gray, smooth, ¼ in. thick; inner bark pale yellow.

Wood.—White or pale yellow; no demarcation between sapwood and heartwood; rays 150 per in., dark brown, straight; pores 2,800 to 5,000 per sq. in., in dense and sparse zones; parenchyma in lines connecting pores; grain resembles walnut; specific gravity 0.898; cuts hard; good for general construction but subject to a blue stain.

Occurrence.—Along coast to 1,000 ft.; Galley Reach, Buna, Kumusi Valley, foot hills of Hydrographer's Range (New Guinea), there are several species in the genus found from sea level to several thousand feet elevation in New Guinea, Bismarck Archipelago and the Solomon Islands.

Moraceae

(Mulberry Family)

113. Tree and shrubs widely distributed throughout the warmer parts of the world; usually distinguished by the milky sap in the inner bark. Buds are scaly or naked. Leaves are stalked, alternate, simple, entire dentate or lobated. Fruits are fleshy or dry and are formed by a consolidation of many flowers. The bark of many species afford valuable fibers as, for example, hemp; other species produce rubber, dyes, hops and edible fruit.

Artocarpus cumingiana (Fig.13)

Local Names.—Kamandag, kubi, pakak (Cagayan); ubien (Ilocos Norte, Abra, Isabela, Pangasinan); kalauahan (Moun Province); ambung (Isabela); anabien (Pangasinan); pintug (Zambales); analiong (Rizal); anibiong, kilian, sulipa (Bataan); anubing, tagop, togop (Tayabas); kunubling (Camarines Sur); anubling, kubi (Albay, Sorsogon); kalulotor, kanet (Mindoro); kili-kili (Samar, Leyte); bayako (Iloilo); bayogo, bayuko (Negros Occidental).

Habit.—A medium sized tree to 50 in. in diameter and 90 ft. in height.

Leaves.—4 to 8 in. by 9 to 17 in., hairy beneath and on veins above.

Flowers.—Without apparent petals.

Fruit.—Fleshy, about size and shape of a strawberry, borne on a stem about 2 in. long.

Bark.—¼ to ½ in. thick, light orange to dark orange-red, papery in young trees, in older ones hard and sheds in small patches; inner bark pink; when cut, exudes milky sap that thickens rapidly on exposure.

Wood.—Sapwood light tan, demarcated from the heartwood which is bright yellow when fresh, turning brown or nearly black with age; rays broad, few in number, often with white deposits; pores large, solitary, diffuse; tyloses and sometimes chalky white deposits present; parenchyma aggregated about the pores in form of a circle or oval; specific gravity, air-dry, 0.548 to 0.969, average 0.725; straight-grained, texture fairly coarse, without characteristic taste or odor; moderately hard, strong, and not liable to checking, but may warp during seasoning; difficult to work but very durable under any conditions;

suitable for all purposes requiring strength and durability, such as for house corner posts, telephone poles, piling, railroad ties, bridge timbers, etc.; difficult to saw into lumber and therefore should be used in the round.

Occurrence.—Philippines. Widely distributed from northern Luzon to Palawan and Mindanao at low and medium altitudes, but is not abundant; other species in this genus present in New Guinea.

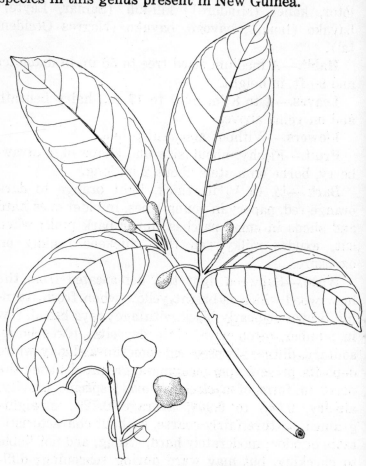

FIGURE 13.–*Artocarpus cumingiana*

Artocarpus incisa

Local Names.—Breadfruit tree. Sakeri (Suku, New Guinea). Form without seeds: soekoen (Malayan); koehoekoe, namoe, saekoen, koeroer, koloeb sarangen (N. Celebes); amoe (Gorontalo, Boelo); tehoe'oe bakare (Bonerate); bakara (Makassar); baka (Boegina); soekoen (Kai I.); soeoene (Ceram, Ambon, Oeliaser, Boeroe); amo (N. Halmahera), Form with seeds: gomo (Ternate, Tidore); gomoe, kelawi, koeloer (Malayan); soekoen batoe (Ambon); koka (Sangir); koka, tamonok, kominsi, koeloeb (N. Celebes); bitila, bitina (Gorontalo); kamojango (Boelo); komontji (Baree); gamasi (Makassar); oelo (Boegina); hoekoen (Kai I.); limes, oemasi, nimasi, oeroele, saoene hoewe (Ceram); soeoen hatoe (Oeliasar); dolai, gogomo (S. and N. Halmahera); baraw, toe (Marind).

Habit—A medium sized tree, attains 3 ft. in diameter and 70 ft. in height; main stem usually short; forms a large, round crown.

Leaves.—Simple, large, rough, dark green, divided into large lobes.

Flowers.—Male flowers borne in long, club-shaped spikes, and female ones in round heads.

Fruit.—A large fleshy mass somewhat like osage orange, green or yellow, may be as much as 3 ft. long and weigh 40 lbs., borne on upper trunk or larger branches; seeds resemble chestnuts and are roasted and eaten; the pulpy mass is baked and eaten—it is a widely used food throughout the region.

Wood.—Heartwood bright yellow, darkens with age, growth rings indistinct; rays fine, numerous and irregularly spaced; pores small to medium, single or in small clusters, irregularly scattered; parenchyma surrounding the pores and in faint concentric

59

lines; soft to hard, heavy and fairly strong; texture is coarse but is not difficult to work and it seasons well; durable; has been used for house construction, shipbuilding, furniture and musical instruments; yields a yellow dye.

Occurrence.—Has been widely distributed by planting throughout the region; common in New Guinea.

Olacaceae

(Olax Family)

Trees and shrubs, with alternate, simple leaves; flowers small, variously arranged; fruit a 1-seeded drupe; there are 22 genera and about 260 species in the family.

FLOWER 4

FRUIT +

0 1 2 3 4
INCHES

FIGURE 14. *Strombosia javanica*

Strombosia javanica (Fig. 14)

Local Names. Dedali, dali dali, bayam badak (Malay Peninsula) ; leke-leke (Nias I., off N.W. Sumatra) ; enteloeng, katjang-katjang, petaling bemban (Malayan) ; menteroengan (Billiton I., off S.E. Sumatra) ; kajoe katjang, madang kalawar, sanam-sanam (West central Sumatra) ; ki katjang (Sunda Is.).

Habit. Generally a small or medium-sized tree; may attain 70 ft. in height and 48 in. in diameter; trunk is straight and without buttresses; crown is compact and dense.

Leaves. Simple, alternate, entire, 4 to 7 in. long, 1½ to 2½ in. wide, elliptical, sharply pointed, rounded at base, glabrous and pale green on both sides; petiole ½ to 1 in. long.

Flowers. Small, borne at axils of the leaves.

Fruit. Green, oblong, ½ in. in diameter and 1 in. long, with soft fleshy coating.

Bark. Yellow or gray, with fine, shallow fissures; freshly exposed surface yellow; ½ in. thick; outer bark corky and brittle, about 0.1 in. thick; sap is watery.

Wood. Light, soft, fine-grained, pale brown or yellow; sapwood not clearly demarcated from heartwood; very durable considering its rather low density; used for construction and cabinet work; is liable to split if not carefully seasoned.

Occurrence. Widely distributed but not abundant and liable to be sporadic; may compose about 1 percent of the volume of the stand; found on low hills and on land just above flood level, sea level to 1,000-ft. elevation; Malay Peninsula, and the Archipelago with several closely allied species.

Anonaceae

Trees and shrubs, with watery juice, often emitting an aromatic or heavy disagreeable odor when bruised. Nearly all representatives are confined to the tropics. Leaves are deciduous, membranous, alternate, and entire. Fruits are usually fleshy, edible, and sugary, but some are dry, aromatic, or pungent, like peppers. Flowers of a Philippine species *(Cananga odorata)* afford an essential oil called ylang-ylang used in perfumery. Root wood of a number of species is light in weight, soft, and often used in place of cork as floats for fishing nets.

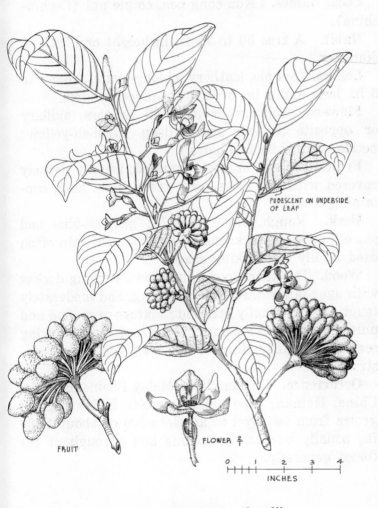

PUBESCENT ON UNDERSIDE OF LEAF

FRUIT

FLOWER $\frac{2}{1}$

0 1 2 3 4
INCHES

FIGURE 15. *Mitrephora thorelii*

Mitrephora thorelii (Fig. 15)

Local Names. Kda cong ben, co gie nui (Cochinchina).

Habit. A tree 50 to 75 ft. in height and 2 ft. in diameter.

Leaves. Simple, leathery, oblong-ovate, from 3 to 6 in. long and 2 in. broad; prominent midrib.

Flowers. Solitary or in small clusters, axillary or opposite a leaf, small, deep purplish-yellow; petals with white fine hairs.

Fruit. Globose or ovoid, stalked, usually densely covered with fine hairs, pale green, 1 in. long, containing 4 seeds.

Bark. Rough, slightly scaly; grayish-blue and smooth on young branches; contains a saponin often used locally for making soap.

Wood. The heartwood light brown turning darker with age; fairly hard, heavy, strong, and moderately tough; grain usually straight; texture very fine and uniform; luster medium; does not split during seasoning; fairly durable; is used for house construction.

Occurrence. Burma, Siam, Malay Peninsula, Indo-China, Hainan; many allied species in the region; grows from sea level to an elevation of about 1,500 ft., usually bordering streams and throughout the forest generally.

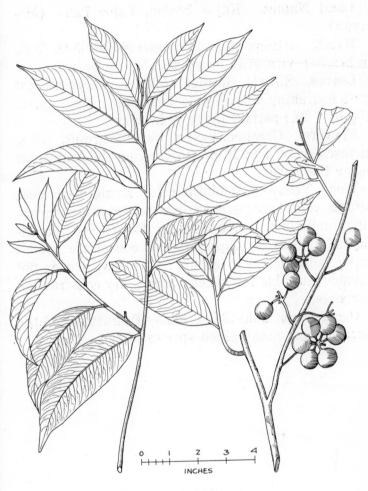

FIGURE 16. *Polyalthia glauca*

Polyalthia glauca (Unona merrittii) (Fig. 16)

Local Names. Kajoe boelan, kajoe kalet (Malayan).

Habit. Attains 18 in. in diameter and 60 to 75 ft. in height; with gray or grayish-brown branches.

Leaves. Simple, elliptical to lanceolate, somewhat leathery, shiny above, pale beneath, 1 by 5 in. to 1½ by 7 in.; petiole about ¼ in. long.

Flowers. Greenish-yellow, very fragrant, borne in fascicles of 4 to 10 or more, along the branchlets below the leaves.

Wood. Yellowish to buff in color: straight-grained; soft to very hard; strong; coarse-textured; growth rings indistinct, demarcated by dense wood; parenchyma in narrow, closely-spaced concentric bands; pores isolated and in groups; rays few, broad; not durable; suitable for general temporary construction purposes.

Occurrence. Indo-China, Malay Peninsula, and the Archipelago; many allied species in the region.

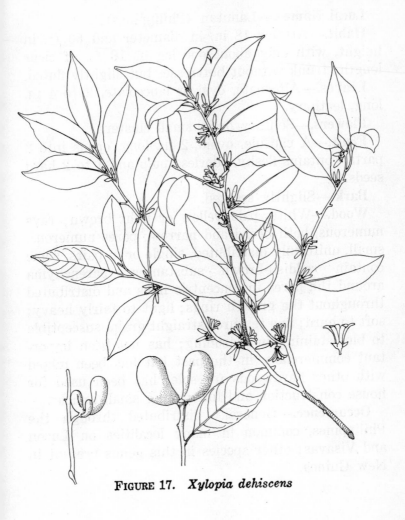

FIGURE 17. *Xylopia dehiscens*

Xylopia dehiscens (Fig. 17)

Local Names.—Lanutan (Philippines).

Habit.—Attains 18 in. in diameter and 60 ft. in height, with only about one log or 16 ft. of clear length; trunk without buttresses but slightly fluted.

Leaves.—Alternate, oval or lanceolate, 2 to 4 in. long, leathery.

Flowers.—Solitary or in small clusters.

Fruit.—A capsule, ovoid, 2 in. long, opens into 3 parts, contains fleshy, odorless pulp and 1 to 2 hard seeds.

Bark.—Slightly scented.

Wood.—White, pale yellow or light brown; rays numerous, both broad and narrow; pores numerous, small, uniformly distributed, single or in pairs, some contain reddish-brown substances; parenchyma around the pores in concentric lines and distributed throughout the growth rings; light to fairly heavy; soft to hard; fine texture; straight grain, susceptible to blue-staining in seasoning; has not been important commercially in the past but has been mixed with other hardwoods for sale; has been used for house construction and for making small articles.

Occurrence.—Generally distributed through the Philippines, common in many localities on Luzon. and Visayas; other species in this genus present in New Guinea.

Myristicaceae

(Nutmeg Family)

Chiefly trees of tropical Asia and America, distinguished by their alternate and smooth-margined leaves which contain valuable aromatic oils; seeds are characterized by their richness in fatty fragrant oils. *Myristica fragrans* is the source of the nutmeg. All representatives of the family have red or yellowish-red sap.

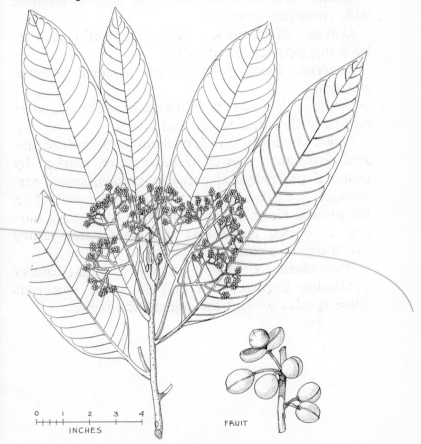

FRUIT

FIGURE 18. *Horsefieldia irya*

71

Horsefieldia irya (Fig. 18)

Local Names. Kandarah, piango, pianggu, lempayan paya, lempoyan paya (Malay Peninsula); soemaralah (Simaloe I., off N.W. Sumatra); peredah boeroeng, pianggoe renah (S.E. Sumatra, Palembang); kalak patjoeng, kiringan, klapan (Java); kadjoe rah (Madura); kanarahan, narahan (S.E. Borneo, Dayak country).

Habit. Attains about 80 ft. in height; slender; wide-spreading branches.

Leaves. Membranous, lanceolate, leathery, 2 in. by 9 in.; petioles, 0.2 in. long.

Flowers. Small, yellow, borne in small terminal clusters.

Fruit. Globose, 1 in. in diameter, glabrous, outer coating yellow and thick, seed round.

Wood. Reddish-brown, medium hard, texture fine, grain straight; growth rings distinct, marked by terminal parenchyma; pores in groups, small, surrounded by parenchyma; parenchyma terminal in the growth rings, narrow to fairly wide; rays narrow to broad, numerous; suitable for temporary construction, boxes, and crates.

Occurrence. Common on moist sites; Malay Peninsula, Borneo, Java and Sumatra; numerous allied species present throughout the region.

MALE FLOWER   FEMALE FLOWER   FRUIT   BURSTED FRUIT

0 1 2 3 4
INCHES

FIGURE 19. *Knema corticosa*

Knema corticosa (Fig. 19)

Habit. A very large tree; young branches gray and covered with soft fine hairs.

Leaves. Simple, membranous to leathery, smooth above, smooth and with whitish bloom below, narrow-lanceolate to broad-lanceolate, 1 by 4 in. to 3 by 8 in.; petioles ½ in. long and channelled on the upper surface.

Flowers. Arranged in small clusters in the axils of the leaves, 1 to 6 flowers per cluster, male flowers with 11 to 13 stamens; female flowers hairy.

Fruit. Although the fruit resembles the nutmeg of commerce it is not an article of trade; downy, ¾ by 1 in.

Bark. Thin, grayish- or yellowish-brown, with scales.

Wood. Reddish-brown, medium hard, heavy, strong; texture fine, grain straight; growth rings distinct, marked by terminal parenchyma; vessels in groups, small, surrounded by parenchyma; parenchyma terminal in the growth rings, narrow to fairly wide; rays narrow to broad, numerous; suitable for temporary construction, boxes, and crates.

Occurrence. Found up to 3,000-ft. elevation; extends through Burma, Malay Peninsula, Siam, Java, Borneo, and Indo-China; numerous similar allied species present in the region.

FIGURE 20.—*Knema glomerata*

Knema glomerata (Fig. 20)

Local Names—Dagdagan, dumadara, panigan, taligahan (Cagayan) ; dumadaga (Mountain Province) ; duguan (Zambales, Bataan, Tayabas, Negros, Davao) ; dalinas, hindurugo-lalaki, matumbao-lalaki, tambalau, tambalau-lalaki (Bataan) ; dagi, parugan (Rizal) ; maragabulo (Rizal, Laguna) ; durugo, ditabutiki, lapak (Laguna) ; tambalau (Batangas) ; lago (Palawan) ; duguan (Surigao).

Habit.—Attains 7½ in. in diameter and 75 ft. height with a main stem of 25 to 35 ft.; cylindrical trunk.

Leaves.—Alternate, 2 to 4 in. long, rigid or leathery, smooth, bright green.

Flowers.—Small, borne in panicles.

Fruit.—Small, juicy; with a single seed.

Wood.—Sapwood reddish-brown, not demarcated from the reddish-brown heartwood; growth rings distinct, marked by terminal parenchyma; rays moderately broad, numerous; pores in groups of 2 to 3, surrounded by narrow rings of parenchyma; parenchyma terminal at the ends of growth rings, moderately narrow; specific gravity, air-dry 0.495 to 0.697, average 0.597; texture fine; glossy; without characteristic odor or taste; light to comparatively heavy, soft and weak, seasons well, easy to work, is easily damaged by termites and fungi. It is used for temporary construction, posts, crates, and other purposes which do not require strength or durability.

Occurrence.—Philippines; widely distributed from the Babuyanens to Mindanao in forests at 150 to 1,500 ft. elevation, common but not abundant; also in Celebes, Moluccas and New Guinea.

FIGURE 21.—*Myristica hollrungii.*

Myristica hollrungii (Fig. 21)

Local Name.—Nutmeg mangrove.

Habit.—Attains 2 ft. in diameter and 100 ft. in height; has flying buttress prop roots similar to mangrove; open crown.

Leaves.—Large.

Fruit.—Yellow, open to expose reddish or yellowish interior; characteristic nutmeg seed.

Bark.—Gray to light brown; inner bark reddish; exudes red sap when cut.

Wood.—Pale in color, straight-grained, cuts clean; suitable for temporary construction.

Occurrence.—Papua and Northeast New Guinea; obtainable in fair quantity along some rivers; this is one of many species in this genus occurring at low to medium altitudes.

Myristica pseudo-argentea

Local Name.—Inene (Sageri, Northern Division, New Guinea).

Habit.—Attains 2½ ft. in diameter and 100 ft. in height with 80 ft. of clear length; small buttresses on spur roots.

Leaves.—Simple, alternate; petiole 1 to 2 in. long; blade 1 to 2 ft. long by 5 to 9 in. broad; oblanceolate, acuminate, leathery, whitish bloom on lower side, upper surface shiny; veins and petiole have rusty, fine hairs.

Fruit.—2 by 2½ in. on stout peduncle ½ in. long; yellow-brown, velvety; splits in two at maturity, contains one seed enveloped in slender tapering filaments.

Bark.—Mottled gray and green; papery scales; inner bark brown streaked with white; exudes sap when cut.

Wood.—Sapwood pale yellow gradually merging with the rose-colored heartwood; rays 200 per in., yellow, sinuous around pores, appear as small specks on radial surface; pores clear, 2,500 to 4,000 per sq. in.; parenchyma in concentric lines, broader than rays, 20 per in.; grain resembles mahogany; specific gravity 0.562; cuts firm.

Lauraceae

(Laurel Family)

Trees and shrubs of the temperate and tropical climates; distinguished by the presence in all parts of the plants of essential oils used extensively in medicine and perfumes; some species yield cloves, cassia, cinnamon, and other aromatic bark; a few species produce camphor.

0 1 2 3 4
INCHES

FIGURE 22. *Cinnamomum iners*

Cinnamomum iners (Fig. 22)

Local Names. Lelang, medang kemangi, singga betina, kajoe tedja, teja badak, kayu manis, kayu manis hutan (Malay Peninsula); kitedja (Sunda Is.); tedja (Java).

Habit. Attains 40 ft. in height; has a short, thick trunk and large bushy crown.

Leaves. White when young, changing to red and finally to dark green, elliptical, leathery, 1 by 5 in. to 3 by 7 in.; petioles ¼ in. long, with prominent longitudinal nerves.

Flowers. Small, yellow, borne in loose panicles which are about 6 in. long.

Fruit. An ellipsoid, black, pulpy, ½ in. long.

Bark. Slightly aromatic, used by Malays in curry.

Wood. Light reddish-brown, occasionally with bands of light brown; strongly scented; light in weight; crossed grain and fine texture; growth rings distinct; pores mainly in groups, small, fairly nuerous; parenchyma surrounding the pores, narrow; oil cells present but empty; rays narrow, few in number; suitable for house construction and cabinet work.

Occurrence. Common on low, moist, open sites throughout the Malay Peninsula; also Sumatra, Java and Borneo; several similar allied species present in the region.

Cinnamomum massoia

Local Names.—Asiru (Suku); api-api (Motu); pai-isa (Vailala); pausa (Buna).

Habit.—Attains 40 in. in diameter and 125 ft. in height with 75 ft. of main stem. Average dimensions are about 30 in. in diameter and 60 ft. of main stem; without buttresses.

Leaves.—Simple, alternate, may be nearly opposite; petiole ¼ in. to ¾ in., small; blade obovate or oblanceolate, with smooth margins; whitish on lower side, dull green on upper side.

Flowers.—Small, green or yellow.

Fruit.—Berry-like, contains a single seed.

Bark.—Greenish-brown, ½ in. thick; inner bark reddish-brown, fragrant odor.

Wood.—Light brown in color, sapwood not sharply demarcated from heartwood; rays yellow, appear as small specks on radial surface; pores fairly dense; cuts soft and wooly; specific gravity, air dry, 0.385; is light, soft and has a fragrant cinnamon odor.

Occurrence.—New Guinea, Veimauri, Vanapa, Buna District, Hydrographer's Range, Opi, and Kumusi; occurs on the plains and foothills up to about 1,500 ft. in elevation.

Cinnamomum mercadoi (Fig. 23)

Local Names.—Kasio (Babuyanes); kuliuan, kasio (Cagayan); pilling, anis (Ilocos Norte); kandaroma (Ilocos Norte, Ilocos Sur, Mountain Province); kanela (Mountain Province, Pangasinan, Camarines, Albay); kariñgañgat, kaliñgad (Pampanga); kailiñgag (Pampanga, Polillo, Rizal, Laguna, Camarines, Lanoa); samiling, semiling (Bataan); kanilan (Camarines); bayaska (Albay); kaniñgag (Samar, Leyte, Cebu, Surigao, Lanao, Davao); kulunion (Zamboanga).

Habit.—A small to medium sized tree attaining 40 in. diameter and 90 ft. height, with straight, cylindrical trunk and only small buttresses.

Leaves.—Leathery; 4 to 8 in. long; glossy above but with whitish bloom below; veins longitudinal.

Flowers.—Small.

Fruit.—Fleshy, black, ovoid, adheres to cup-shaped remains of flower, $\frac{1}{2}$ to $\frac{3}{4}$ in. in diameter.

Bark.—Thin, gray, corky; inner bark red, aromatic odor.

Wood.—Sapwood light tan, not sharply demarcated from the darker heartwood; rays narrow, few in number; pores in groups of 2 to 4, diffuse, small, fairly numerous, occasionally tyloses and white deposits are present; parenchyma in narrow rings about the pores, some with winglike lateral extensions; oil cells are diffuse around and occur with the parenchyma; specific gravity air-dry 0.538; texture fine; grain crossed; has strong sassafras odor, comparatively light and soft, fairly strong, seasons well, resistant to insects but only moderately durable in contact with the ground. It is used for house construction and cabinet work, for lining chests and wardrobes.

Occurrence.—Philippines; widely distributed from the Babuyan Islands to Mindanao; common in forests at low and medium altitudes and has been logged in the past at several points. Other species in the genus are present in New Guinea.

FIGURE 23. –*Cinnamomum mercadoi*

84

FIGURE 24. *Cinnamomum parthenoxylon*

Cinnamomum parthenoxylon (Fig. 24)

Local Names. Medang, medang kemangi, medang busok, medang losoh, medang gatal, medang serai, chintamula hitam, gadis, kajoe gadis, kajoe lada, kayu gadis (Malay Peninsula); laso (Sumatra); kepaleh, rawali (Borneo); hoeroe pedes, ki pedes, ki sereh, melana (Sunda Is.); selasihan (Java).

Habit. Attains 100 ft. in height.

Leaves. Red when young, dark green, leathery when mature, elliptical or ovate, 1 in. by 2 in. to 1¾ in. by 4 in., petioles 1 in. long.

Flowers. Borne in panicles, light yellow, 0.1 in. in diameter.

Fruit. A globose drupe, ¼ in. in diameter.

Bark. Whitish and rough.

Wood. Light reddish-brown, occasionally with bands of light brown; strongly scented, light in weight, crossed grain, and fine texture; growth rings are distinct; pores mainly in groups, small, fairly numerous; parenchyma surrounding the pores, narrow; oil cells present but empty; rays narrow, few in number; suitable for house construction and cabinet work.

Occurrence. In hilly districts; Malay Peninsula, Indo-China and Southern China.

Cryptocarya densiflora (Fig. 25)

Habit. Attains 15 to 20 in. in diameter and 40 to 60 ft. in height.

Leaves. Dark green, leathery, elliptical, whitish below, 3 by 8 in.; petioles ¼ in. long.

Flowers. Yellowish-red, borne in panicles.

Fruit. Globose, ¾ in. in diameter.

Wood. Wood light in color, sapwood not sharply demarcated from the heartwood; hard and heavy; fine-textured, straight-grained; growth rings distinct, marked by terminal parenchyma; pores solitary and in groups, small, few in number; parenchyma terminal in the growth rings; oil cells distinct and filled with yellow deposits; rays broad, few to numerous; suitable for general construction purposes.

Occurrence. Malay Peninsula, Java, and Borneo; many similar allied species present in primary forests of the region.

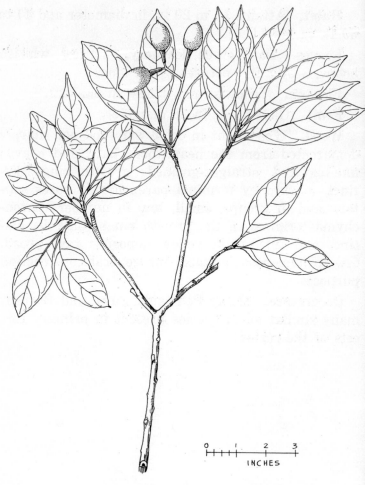

FIGURE 26. *Dehaasia cairocan*

Dehaasia cairocan (Beilschmiedia cairocan)
(Fig. 26)

Habit. A medium-sized tree with a short, straight, cylindrical trunk, often 3 ft. in diameter at the base, without buttresses; crown spreading and forming a dense head.

Leaves. Simple, with smooth margins, leathery, often with a pale violet hue on the lower side, acute, elliptic-lanceolate, 2 by 4 in. to 5 to 8 in., midrib prominent on under surface; petiole ½ to 1 in. long; borne in fascicles at the ends of branches.

Flowers. Greenish, small, borne on pedicels, ½ to ¾ in. long, in panicles with 3 to 6 flowers.

Fruit. An ovate berry, ½ to 1 in. long, dark blue.

Bark. Grayish on main trunk; white bark on the leafy twigs.

Wood. Sapwood pale, not sharply demarcated from the gray to brownish heartwood; growth rings not distinct, but there is a visible demarcation due to the difference in density in early and late wood; pores solitary or in groups of 2 to 4, arranged radially, diffuse, some arranged in echelon formation, fairly numerous, most contain tyloses; wood parenchyma abundant or not conspicuous; oil cells few in number, not conspicuous; rays of uniform width, narrow, few in number; cross-grained, fine-textured; glossy; with a pungent odor similar to vinegar when freshly cut; fairly heavy, hard, and strong; specific gravity, air-dry, 0.668; seasons well, very easy to work and to carve; durable when exposed and in contact with the ground; suitable for general construction and cabinet work, carving, house posts, and for all purposes where a strong, durable wood is desired.

Occurrence. Hainan; similar allied species present in Burma, Siam, Indo-China, Malay Peninsula, and Archipelago.

FIGURE 25. *Cryptocarya densiflora*

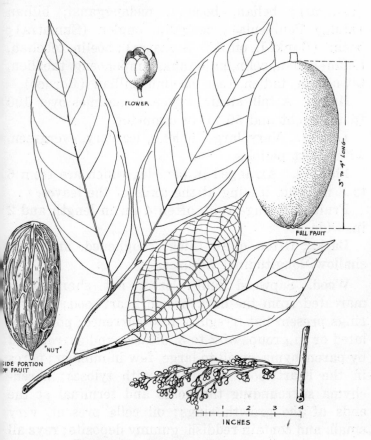

FLOWER

FULL FRUIT

3" to 4" LONG

"NUT"

SIDE PORTION
OF FRUIT

0 1 2 3 4
INCHES

FIGURE 27. *Eusideroxylon zwageri*

Eusideroxylon zwageri (Fig. 27)

Local Names. Ijzerhout (common term in Dutch on Borneo and S.E. Sumatra) ; Borneo ironwood (general) ; belian, boelian, melangganai, billian (Malay Peninsula) ; oengaliu, onglen (Sumatra) ; boelin (Banki I., off S.E. Sumatra) ; boelin, tebelian, telian, balian, oelin, kajo taha, lampahoeng, tabalien, tawoedien, tadien, caju baelian, billian (Borneo).

Habit. A tall, straight tree, sometimes over 100 ft. in height and 50 in. in diameter.

Leaves. Very large, oblong, leathery, evergreen, with short petioles.

Flowers. Arranged in panicles which are from 6 to 8 in. long, issuing at the axils of the leaves.

Fruit. Oblong-ovoid, often 4 in. in length and 2 in. wide.

Bark. Often quite thick, roughened, and with shallow, longitudinal fissures.

Wood. Sapwood buff-colored, not sharply demarcated from the dark brown heartwood; growth rings present but irregular in occurrence; pores isolated or in groups of 2 to 3, diffuse, and surrounded by parenchyma, small to large, few in number; pores in the heartwood well filled with tyloses; parenchyma surrounding the pores and terminal at the ends of the growth rings; oil cells present, very small, and contain reddish, gummy deposits; rays all about the same width, narrow, few in number; grain straight or slightly crossed; texture fine; glossy; without characteristic odor or taste; very heavy, hard, and strong; specific gravity, air-dry, 0.834 to 1.137, average 1.032; seasons well but is difficult to work because of its hardness; very durable, is resistant to the attack of marine borers; has been used for high-grade construction where durability and strength are required, for wharf and bridge timbers, salt-water piling, etc. In Borneo it is probably the best known and highest valued wood due to its durability and strength.

Occurrence. Mainly in Borneo but reported also in Malay Peninsula.

FIGURE 28. *Litsea glutinosa*

93

Litsea glutinosa (L. sebifera) (Fig. 28)

Local Names. Sablot (Philippines); ondon (Burma); malek (Malay Peninsula); malai (Banka I., off E. Sumatra); malih (W. Borneo); hoeroe tangkalak (Sunda Is.); woeroe lilin (Java).

Habit. Generally a small tree but attains 24 in. in diameter and 60 ft. in height in Philippines.

Leaves. Simple, elliptical or ovate, 5 to 8 in. long, lustrous, dark green above, light blue and pubescent below, thick and leathery, aromatic when crushed; petioles about 1 in. long.

Flowers. Greenish-gray, downy, borne in short racemes or in cymes at leaf axils.

Fruit. A small, fleshy, brown berry; about ¼ in. in diameter, with single seed; has persistent cup-like base.

Bark. Gray, smooth, thin and corky; inner bark red; branchlets gray and downy.

Wood. Light red, fine-textured but cross grained; soft to medium hard; growth rings irregular and indistinct; pores few, arranged in pairs or small groups, filled with deposits; parenchyma in rings about the pores; oil cells empty; rays fine and inconspicuous; specific gravity, 0.721; considered generally durable and resistant to insect attack, has been used for house corner posts and agricultural implements.

Occurrence. Widely distributed throughout the region up to about 700 ft. elevation; New Guinea, the Philippines, Burma, Malay Peninsula and Archipelago, southern China; numerous allied species also present in the region.

Litsea grandifolia

Local Names.—Toranu (Suku).

Habit.—A small tree, 20 in. in diameter and 35 ft. tall.

Leaves.—Simple, alternate; petiole 2½ in. long, blade 6 x 18 in., oblanceolate, with minute hairs on lower side, smooth on upper side; bunched at ends of the twigs.

Flowers.—In clusters of 2 to 5, borne in axils of leaves, greenish yellow.

Fruit.—Small and round or elongated berry-like.

Wood.—Heartwood gray or brown, without odor, soft to hard, fine grained, works well, subject to staining and should be carefully seasoned.

Occurrence—New Guinea.

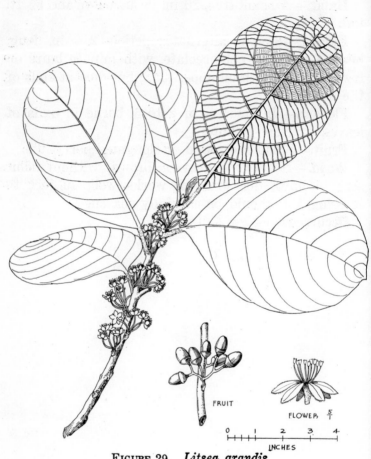

FRUIT

FLOWER $\frac{5}{7}$

0 1 2 3 4
INCHES

FIGURE 29. *Litsea grandis*

96

Litsea grandis (Fig. 29)

Local Names. Medang busuk, medang busok, medang telor, medang daun lebar (Malay Peninsula).

Habit. Attains 60 to 100 ft. in height; bushy crown; branchlets brown-velvety.

Leaves. Obovate, stiffly leathery, smooth above, with fine red hairs below, 3 in. by 7 in.; petioles ½ to ¾ in. long.

Flowers. Yellow, borne in short racemes.

Fruit. Elliptical, ¾ in. long.

Wood. Wood light yellow or reddish-yellow, occasionally grayish-brown; moderately soft, cross-grained, fine-textured; somewhat scented; very easy to work; growth rings are indistinct; pores mainly in groups, diffuse, may be arranged in echelon formation, small in size, few in number; parenchyma surrounding the pores, empty oil cells present; rays narrow, few in number; suitable for general construction, carving, and patternmaking.

Occurrence. Common in open country; Malay Peninsula, Burma, Java; several similar allied species present in the region.

Hernandiaceae

(Hernandia Family)

Trees and shrubs with smooth, alternate, entire or lobed, petioled leaves. There are probably less than 40 little-known species classified within this family, but they are widely distributed throughout the tropical parts of both hemispheres. Fruits are dry, one-seeded, and winged. All parts of the plants contain oil cells; the juice of the leaves of some species is a powerful depilatory, destroying hair without pain. The wood is soft and light in weight.

FIGURE 30.—*Gyrocarpus americanus*

Gyrocarpus americanus (Fig. 30)

Local Names.—Philippines: lapo-lapo (Ilocos Sur, Abra); malasapsap (Nueva Ecija, Rizal); kulong-kulong (Marinduque); tangisang-bayauak (Lubang).

Habit.—A medium size tree, attaining 36 in. diameter and 75 ft. height.

Leaves.—Deciduous, simple, alternate, large, sometimes lobed, with long petioles.

Flowers.—Borne in dense panicles, small, greenish; appear before the new leaves.

Fruit.—Small, nut-like and two-winged at the apex.

Wood.—Sapwood tan, not sharply demarcated from the brownish heartwood; rays moderately broad, few in number; pores solitary and in groups, moderately large; glossy, wavy grained, coarse textured, light, soft, seasons well, is resistant to insects but not to decay; suitable for light furniture and general repair work for which a light, soft wood is suitable; has not been widely utilized in the past.

Occurrence.—In Celebes, Moluccas, New Guinea and Luzon, Mindoro, Lubang, Marinduque and Palawan in the Philippines; generally near the seashore and on dry slopes inland; common on Lubang Island.

FIGURE 31. *Hernandia ovigera*

Hernandia ovigera (Fig. 31)

Local Names. Eierboom, bengkak (Java). Philippines: malatangan-tangan, pantoglobo (Tayabas); banago (Batangas); kolon-kogon, koron-koron (Camarines); indang (Rizal); malatapai (Negros Occidental); taba-taba (Cataduanes Is.); kolong-kolong (Zamboanga); kung-kung (Basilan). New Guinea: kuyuyu (Buna); kerea (Suku); baraida (Vailala); aputz (Yalu).

Habit. A large tree attaining 50 in. in diameter.

Leaves. Smooth, heart-shaped, simple, alternate, 4 to 5 in. long; petiole attached at about ½ in, from base of blade; pale green below, leathery.

Flowers. Borne in panicles, yellowish, male and female flowers on same tree.

Fruit. Single-seeded, small, dry; surrounded by a loose, fleshy outer coat, resembling a small Japanese lantern.

Wood. Sapwood tan, not sharply demarcated from the grayish-brown heartwood; growth rings indistinct; rays moderately broad, few in number; pores solitary and in groups of 2 to 6, diffuse, moderately small; parenchyma in rings about the pores, broad, with winglike lateral extensions; oil cells indistinct; specific gravity, air-dry, 0.434; grain straight, texture fairly coarse; pungent odor when fresh; light, soft, not strong; seasons easily, easy to work, durable for interior work but not when exposed; has been used for furniture, cabinet work, fish net floats, drawing boards, and musical instruments.

Occurrence. Found along seacoasts only; Malay Peninsula and Archipelago, Indo-China. In Philippines in central to southern Luzon, Catanduanes, Mindoro, Negros, Palawan, Balabac, Camiguin, Surigao, Dinagal, Lanao, Davao, Zamboanga, Basilan, Bancalan, and Jolog. In New Guinea along the seacoast of the Northern Division, Veimauri foothills and Baroi alluvial flats.

Hernandia peltata

Local Names.—Jack-in-a-box tree. Kuyuyu (Buna) ; kerea (Suku) ; baraida (Vailala) ; aputz (Yalu) ; kampe, mata ikan (Malayan) ; naoemalako (N. Halmahera) ; njalako (Ternate) ; njalaoe (Tidore).

Habit.—Attains 30 in. diameter.

Leaves.—Simple, alternate; petiole 4 to 5 in. long, blade 4 to 6 in. by 6 to 8 in.; petiole attached to blade at about ½ in. from base; smooth and shiny on upper side, pale green on lower side; leathery.

Flowers.—Borne in axillary panicles.

Fruit.—A capsule 3/16 by 1 in. with a fleshy, light green, translucent envelope. Flowers and fruits in July and August in Northern Division.

Bark.—Gray, ridged and scaly.

Wood.—White; sapwood not sharply demarcated from heartwood; rays sinuous, are scarely visible on radial surface; pores fairly numerous; parenchyma in broken, concentric lines, connecting and surrounding pores; specific gravity, 0.417; cuts soft, is used by natives for making canoes.

Occurrence.—New Guinea, along the seacoast of Northern Division, Veimauri foothills and Baroi alluvial flats.

Rosaceae

(Rose Family)

Trees, shrubs, and herbs indigenous to all parts of the world, though more sparingly dispersed within the tropics. It includes over 2,000 species with widely different characters; a number of species afford important fruits. A South American genera *(Quillaia)* affords the commercial soap bark of Chile which furnishes a saponin similar to that of *Pometia pinnata* of the South Pacific Islands.

Figure 32. *Parinarium corymbosum*

Parinarium corymbosum (Fig. 32)

Local Names. Kajoe batoe, merbatoe lojang, soengko bimau (Malayan); kalek koereseng, kalek parada (West central Sumatra); taritig (Sunda Is.); soeloeh, triwoelan, woeloh (Java).

Habit. A large tree, attaining 80 in. in diameter and a height of 50 ft.; the trunk is straight and cylindrical with small buttresses; branches are thick.

Leaves. Simple, 5 to 6 in. long, narrowed at the base.

Flowers. About ½ in. in diameter, on short peduncles, borne in panicles.

Fruit. An obovoid drupe, 1 to 1¼ in. long, 2-celled.

Bark. Black.

Wood. Sapwood light in color; heartwood reddish-brown; growth rings indistinct; pores nearly all solitary, diffuse, with some in echelon formation, small to large, tyloses seldom present; parenchyma in concentric bands, very narrow, numerous; rays of 2 distinct widths but both very narrow; grain wavy, texture coarse; dull in appearance; without characteristic odor or taste; very heavy, hard, and strong; specific gravity, air-dry, 0.988; seasons well with little checking but is liable to warp if not carefully handled; difficult to saw and to work with tools; greasy feel when cut; resistant to attacks of marine borers and moderately durable when exposed to the weather or in contact with the ground; recommended for salt-water piling because of its resistance to marine borers, although an outer coating of creosote and asphalt is recommended; is also used for construction where strength is important, and should be used in the round, without sawing.

Occurrence. Common and fairly abundant in forests at low to medium altitudes; Burma, Malay Peninsula, and Archipelago.

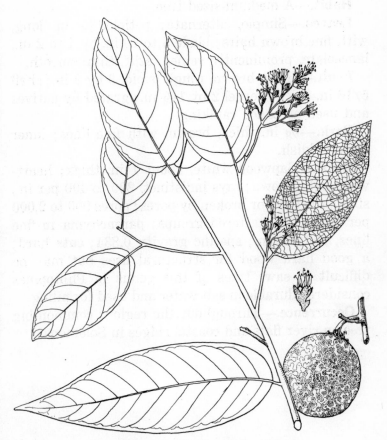

FIGURE 33. *Parinarium glaberrimum*

107

Parinarium glaberrimum (*P. laurimum*)
(Fig. 33)

Local Names.—Atoeng (Malayan) ; lomo (Makassar) ; samaka (Boegina) ; saja (Ternate).

Habit.—A medium-sized tree.

Leaves.—Simple, alternate; petiole ⅜ in. long, with fine brown hairs; blade 5 to 10 in. by 1 to 2 in., lanceolate, prominently veined, stiff, thin, smooth.

Fruit.—Hard, brown, rough ovoid, 3 by 2 in.; shell 5/16 in. thick; kernel 2 by 1½ in.; grated by natives and used as canoe caulking.

Bark.—⅛ in. thick, brown, with fine lines; inner bark reddish.

Wood.—Sapwood white, about 1 in. thick; heartwood light brown; rays indistinct, 390 to 400 per in., sinuous around or broken by pores; pores 900 to 2,000 per sq. in. in scattered groups; parenchyma in fine lines, 250 per in.; specific gravity 0.834; cuts hard; a good hard wood for structural uses but may be difficult to saw; trees of this genus in Philippines considered durable in salt water and used for piling.

Occurrence.—Throughout the region; common big tree on river flats and coastal ridges in Solomons.

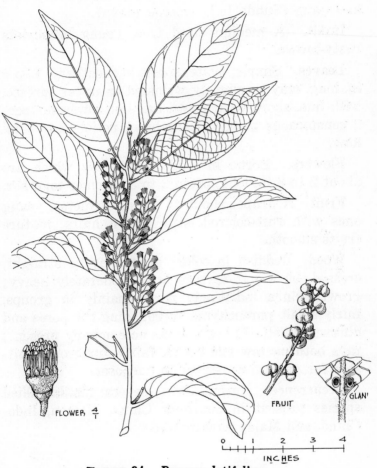

FLOWER $\frac{4}{1}$

FRUIT

GLAN'

0 1 2 3 4
INCHES

FIGURE 34. *Pygeum latifolium*

Pygeum latifolium (P. arboreum) (Fig. 34)

Local Names. Hoeroe menteng, hoeroe mentrek, kawojang (Sunda Is.); woeroe (Java).

Habit. A medium-sized tree, young branchlets rusty-brown.

Leaves. Simple, ovate, somewhat leathery, 4 to 6 in. long, may be slightly wrinkled on upper surface, with fine, short, soft brown hairs on lower surface; 2 conspicuous glands at the base; petiole 2 to 4 in. long.

Flowers. Borne in axillary racemes which are about 2 to 3 in. long, often 2 to 3 racemes together.

Fruit. A drupe, about ½ in. in diameter, young ones with rust-colored, stiff, brown hairs; mature fruits smooth.

Wood. Reddish in color; grain may be straight, crossed, or wavy; texture fine; moderately heavy; growth rings indistinct; pores mainly in groups, fairly small, parenchyma surrounding the pores and diffuse, indistinct; resin ducts occasionally present; rays both narrow and broad, fairly numerous; suitable for general construction purposes.

Occurrence. Burma, Java; several similar allied species present in Southern China, Hainan, Indo-China, and Malay Archipelago.

FIGURE 35. —*Pygeum preslii*

Pygeum preslii (Fig. 35)

Local Names.—Lago.

Habit.—Attains 24 in. diameter and 60 ft. height; clear length of about one log or 16 ft.; trunk without buttresses but slightly fluted.

Leaves.—Alternate, entire, evergreen, glossy above, lighter green below; acid odor when crushed.

Flowers.—In clusters, resembling those of the cherry; individual flowers small and covered with woolly hairs.

Fruit.—A nearly oblong drupe with a kidney-shaped pit or stone.

Wood.—Light reddish-brown, sapwood not sharply demarcated from heartwood; growth rings indistinct, marked by narrow lines of terminal parenchyma; rays very numerous, very fine and hardly visible; pores small, uniformly distributed, solitary, in pairs, in short radial rows, or in concentric lines, the latter type often with reddish-brown deposits; parenchyma surrounding the pores which are in concentric lines; moderately hard and heavy, wavy or curly grain, fine texture, definite odor, seasons well and works easily; has been used for house construction, furniture and cabinet work.

Occurrence.—Widely distributed throughout the Philippines, particularly on Luzon; common from sea level to 3,600 ft. elevation. Other species in the genus are present in New Guinea.

Pygeum vulgare

Local Names.—Apitan, humeg (Cagayan) ; humug (Isabela) ; pamiliñgan (Ilocos Norte) ; marakiteb (Pangasinan) ; paitan (Nueva Ecija) ; duklap (Zambales) ; amugan, amoñgian (Bataan) ; gupit (Rizal) ; lago (Laguna) ; panikin (Tayabas) ; bangluai (Mindoro) ; kanumog (Camarines Sur) ; ipus-ipus (Cebu) ; talegotbon (Bohol) ; kambal (Zamboanga). Commercially called lago.

Habit.—Medium size tree 50 in. diameter, with 45 ft. of clear length; cylindrical trunk.

Leaves.—Simple, ovate, 3 in. long, with entire margins.

Flowers.—Small, white, with woolly hairs, borne in small axillary or lateral clusters, resemble peach blossoms.

Fruit.—A small dry pod with a kidney-shaped seed.

Bark.—Thin, resembles that of our cherry or pear trees.

Wood.—Sapwood light in color, not sharply demarcated from reddish-brown heartwood; growth rings indistinct, but are composed of concentric rings of light and dense wood; rays are both broad and fine, numerous; pores in groups of 2 to 4, diffuse, occasionally contain black, gummy deposits; parenchyma surrounds each vessel in narrow ring, also occurs diffuse, and in narrow bands; gum ducts occasionally present, resemble the vessels and occur in rows of 6 to 10 parallel to the growth rings; grain is wavy and crossed; texture moderately fine; without characteristic odor or taste; glossy, heavy and hard, moderately strong, tough, seasons well, is easy to work, fairly durable for interior use, but not durable when exposed or in contact with the ground.

Occurrence.—Widely distributed from northern Luzon to Mindanao in the Philippines; fairly common in the forests 'at low and medium altitudes.

Leguminosae
(Legume Family)

Trees, shrubs, and herbs widely distributed throughout the temperate and torrid zones of both hemispheres. It is one of the most important family groups, since many of its species afford valuable woods, fibers, gums, dyes, tannins, food products, and drugs. Many species attain large sizes and afford valuable hard and durable woods used for special purposes. Brazil rosewood *(Dalbergia nigra)* is one of the most valuable species.

FIGURE 36.—*Acacia mangium.*

116

Acacia crassicarpa (see Fig. 36 for similar species)

Habit.—Attains 18 in. in diameter and 60 to 70 ft. in height; brown branchlets, petioles and veins of leaves give crown a brownish hue.

Leaves.—A flat expanded petiole instead of a true leaf, gray in color and hooked like a sickle.

Flowers.—Pale yellow, in fluffy spikes.

Fruit.—Slender pods, usually several together; curl and twist as they ripen.

Bark.—Dark gray, thick, hard and deeply fissured; inner bark red.

Wood.—Yellow in color; hard; durable.

Occurrence.—Plentiful on ridges in the savannah forests of Papua; also occurs close behind the mangrove stands and may be one of the principal species in the drier areas of the rain forest; this is one of several species of this genus which occur in Papua and Northeast New Guinea.

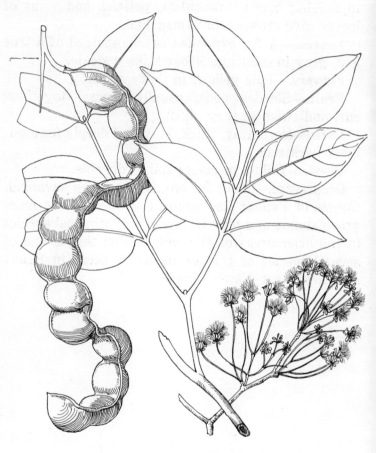

FIGURE 37.—*Albizzia acle*

118

Albizzia acle (Fig. 37)

Local Names.—Kita-kita (Ilocos Norte, Pangasinan, Zambales, Nueva Ecija); tili, tilis (Pangasinan, Zambales); anagap (Zambales); akle (Bulacan, Camarines, Sorsogon, Masbate); mabunga (Laguna); langin (Sorsogon, Masbate); langip (Negros Occidental); labangi (Iloilo); banuyo (Capiz, Negros); langan (Masbate); sauriri, tauriri (Palawan).

Habit.—Attains 50 in. diameter; trunk often short and crooked, without buttresses.

Leaves.—Bipinnately compound, usually with one pair of pinnae, each with 3 to 6 pairs of leaflets, terminal pairs of leaflets much larger than the others; leaflets 1 to 3 in. x 2 to 9 in.

Flowers.—Creamy white and in axillary stalked heads.

Fruit.—A pod, nearly oblong, glabrous from 4 to 8 in. long and 1 to 2 in. wide.

Bark.—Dark brown ¼ to ½ in. thick, covered with thick scales; surface lathers when rubbed with water; inner bark reddish-brown, brittle in texture.

Wood.—Sapwood light brown, sharply demarcated from the darker brown heartwood; grain is crossed, occasionally wavy; texture fine to coarse, without characteristic taste or odor, glossy; dry sawdust causes sneezing; specific gravity air-dry 0.758; heavy and hard; seasons well with very little checking or warping; works easily and takes a high polish; very durable, even in contact with the ground and is resistant to termites. In salt water, however, it is readily damaged by teredo and martesia.

Occurrence.—Philippines, in Northern Luzon (Ilocos Sur) southward to Palawan and Negros, in the forests at low and medium altitudes; widely distributed but available in only small quantities; commonest occurrence in Masbate and Palawan. Other species in the genus are present throughout the region.

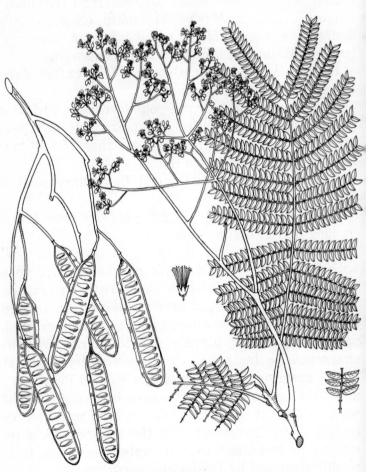

FIGURE 38.—*Albizzia falcata.*

120

Albizzia falcata (Fig. 38)

Local Names. Djeungdjing, djeundgjing laoet (Sunda Islands); kalbi, sengon landi, sengon laoet, sengon sabrang (Java).

Habit. A medium-sized, deciduous, unarmed tree, often 90 ft. in height and 50 in. in diameter; bole short and crown large, round, and spreading.

Leaves. Bipinnately compound; numerous very small leaflets.

Flowers. In globose heads, sessile or on pedicels.

Fruit. A pod, 4 in. long and 1½ in. wide, thin, flat, strap-like, straight, opens normally by 2 valves, with a few seeds.

Bark. Light or grayish, thin, smooth or on old trees slightly fissured; reddish inside, containing much tannin.

Wood. Sapwood thick, light, distinct from the dark reddish-brown heartwood; grain crossed, texture fine to coarse; moderately hard; growth rings distinct, marked by dense late wood; pores diffuse, arranged in oblique rows; parenchyma surrounding the pores; rays very narrow, few in number; seasons well, works easily, and is considered durable even in contact with the ground, but is not resistant to marine borers; is used for furniture.

Occurrence. Mainly on dry uplands, often on sites too poor for other trees to make good growth; widely distributed throughout southern Asia; Burma, Malay Peninsula, Java, Borneo, Siam, Cochinchina.

Albizzia fulva

Local Names.—Gemona (Buna) kerefere (Upper Ramu River), haiede (Vailala).

Habit.—A large tree, to 3½ ft. in diameter and 150 ft. in height, with 80 ft. of clear length.

Leaves.—Bi-pinnately compound, alternate, 9 in. overall; leaflets opposite, without petioles; blade 3/16 by 7/16 in., smooth.

Flowers.—White, in axillary panicles.

Fruit.—A thin pod ½ in. by 5 in.

Bark.—Gray, generally smooth.

Wood.—Pale yellow to dark yellow; sapwood not demarcated from heartwood; rays fine, numerous, pores conspicuous; 500 per sq. in., fairly evenly scattered; straight-grained; cuts soft and woolly; specific gravity 0.290.

Occurrence.—This species found at 3,000 ft. and above on Owen Stanley Range (Papua), probably also elsewhere in the region. The genus is represented by other species in the region, ranging from near sea level to middle elevations in the mountains.

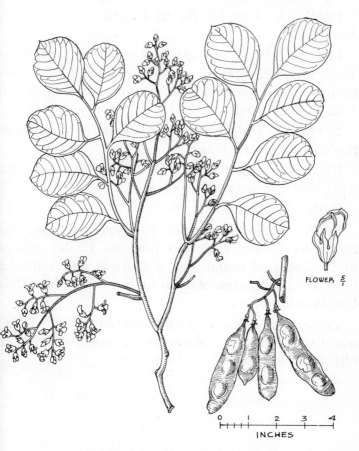

FLOWER $\frac{5}{1}$

0 1 2 3 4
INCHES

FIGURE 39. *Dalbergia latifolia*

123

Dalbergia cochinchinensis
(See Fig. 39 for related species)

Local Names. Trac, trad den, trac vang, trac bong, trac trang, trac mat (Cochinchina).

Habit. Attains 80 ft. in height and 2 ft. in diameter.

Leaves. Pinnately compound, 6 to 8 in. long; leaflets 7 to 9, subopposite, ovate, quite smooth on both surfaces, pale green above, whitish beneath, ¾ by 1 in. to 1 by 2 in.

Flowers. White, ovate, borne in open axillary panicles 3 to 6 in. long.

Fruit. A smooth pod, 2 to 3 in. long and ½ in. wide, bearing a compressed seed.

Bark. Gray, smooth, fibrous.

Wood. Dark red, becoming darker with age; has been occasionally imported into the United States in the form of round logs with bark and sapwood hewn off; a suitable substitute for cocobolo, *(Dalbergia retusa)*.

Occurrence. Common throughout Cochinchina, especially along the Saigon river; numerous similar allied species present in the region.

FIGURE 40. *Intsia bijuga*

Intsia bijuga (Afzelia bijuga) (Fig. 40)

Local Names. Moluccan ironwood (Trade); Moluccan ijzerhout, ipil, merbau changkat, merbaoe (Malay Peninsula); merbo, tariti (Sunda Is.); ipi (Alor or Ombay I.); bendora (Buna, Binendale); kaboing (Yabim, Markham River coast), ombong (Yalu, Lower Markham Valley); sabol (Waria); kwila (Rabaul); melila (Motu); dedira (Suku); pira (Vailala); eh (Evara, Delta Division); lehase (Sangir); ipil, sira, waroeasei, maroeasei, ipil-o (N. Celebes); ipi (Boegina); ai fra mas (Kai I.); isere (W. Ceram); ekelo (S. Ceram); wesele (Ambon, Oeliaser); telat (Boeroe); tos (S. Halmahera); dowora (N. Halmahera, Ternate).

Habit. Attains 3 ft. in diameter and 100 ft. in height, with 50 ft. of clear length; may have buttresses or mangrove-like prop roots, depending upon the site conditions.

Leaves. Compound, alternate; leaflets large, opposite, 2 by 5 in., ovate, glabrous; leaflet petioles ¼ in. long.

Fruit. A flat pod with few seeds.

Bark. Less than ¼ in. thick, light brown, smooth, with scattered large flaky scales.

Wood. Sapwood 2 to 5 in. thick, light yellow; heartwood reddish-brown; rays fine; pores conspicuous, irregularly scattered in zones and surrounded by parenchyma; parenchyma distinct, surrounds pores and connects small groups of pores, also in fine concentric lines; specific gravity, 0.770; cuts hard; durable in contact with the ground and resistant to termites and toredos; used for all structural purposes, including bridges and piling; considered the best hardwood in New Guinea and the Solomons.

Occurrence. Throughout the region; from coasts to 2,000 ft. elevation; local occurrence abundant to scattered; best development is up to 100 ft. elevation close behind beaches and in deep moist river flats.

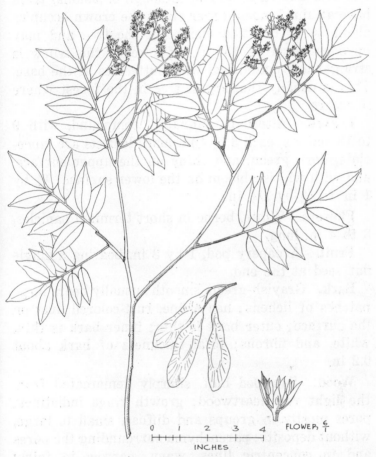

0 1 2 3 4 FLOWER, $\frac{6}{1}$

INCHES

FIGURE 41. *Koompassia excelsa*

Koompassia excelsa (Fig. 41)

Local Names. Tualang (Malay Peninsula).

Habit. Large trees with widespreading crowns and large buttresses; attains about 40 in. in diameter and over 200 ft. in height, although occasional trees have attained much larger sizes; the crown occupies about ½ of the total height of the tree and may have as much as 150 ft. of spread; the trunk is straight and cylindrical with buttresses at the base. This is usually the largest tree in the forest where it occurs.

Leaves. Alternate, pinnately compound, with 9 to 13 leaflets, each 3 to 4 in. long; leaflets are lance-olate, dark green, and shiny on the upper surface, and with whitish bloom on the lower surface; ¼ by 1 in. to ½ by 1½ in.

Flowers. White, borne in short terminal panicles, 3 to 4 in. long.

Fruit. A papery pod, 1 by 3 in. bearing a single flat seed at the end.

Bark. Grayish-green, smooth; usually bears large patches of lichens; has a fine, rust-colored dust on the surface; outer bark is thin; inner bark is thin, white, and fibrous; total thickness of bark about 0.2 in.

Wood. Sapwood buff, sharply demarcated from the light red heartwood; growth rings indistinct; pores mostly in groups and diffuse, small to large, without deposits; parenchyma surrounding the pores and in concentric lines, wavy, narrow to fairly broad; rays few in number; grain crossed, with ribbony appearance on the radial surface; texture

128

coarse; glossy in appearance; without distinct taste or odor; heavy, hard, and tough; specific gravity, air-dry, 0.808; must be carefully seasoned to avoid warping; somewhat difficult to work but takes a high polish; durable in interior work but not considered resistant to decay; splits easily; has not been extensively cut in the past but should be suitable for general construction where strength and toughness are needed, when protected from exposure; burns readily and is used by the natives for making charcoal.

Occurrence. Found in considerable amounts in the forests at low altitudes in stream valleys and lower slopes of foothills; Malay Peninsula, Borneo, and Sumatra.

FRUIT

0 1 2 3 4
INCHES

FIGURE 42. *Koompassia malaccensis*

Koompassia malaccensis (Fig. 42)

Local Names. Garis, enggaris, menggaris, tanggaris, kampas, kempas, oempas (Malayan); toe-alang ajam, toemaling, njari (Sumatra); Pa (East Borneo).

Habit. A large tree of the top forest story, attains 24 in. to 80 in. in diameter and 180 ft. in height with 85 ft. of clear length; the trunk is cylindrical and forms large buttresses; the crown is usually less than ½ the total height of the tree but may spread as much as 100 ft.

Leaves. Pinnately compound, alternate, with 79 leaflets which are dark green above and lighter, often glaucous, beneath; leaflets lanceolate with sharp points, 1 by 2 in. to 1½ by 3 in; petioles 1 to 1½ in. long; overall length of leaf 5 to 8 in.

Flowers. Greenish-white, borne in panicles 3 to 4 in. long.

Fruit. A twisted, papery pod, 4 to 5 in. long, light green or yellowish, bearing a single flat seed; very numerous.

Bark. Gray to black with narrow, longitudinal fissures, 0.3 to 0.4 in. thick; outer bark dark, thin, and brittle; inner bark yellowish-brown and brittle; has the odor of crushed beans.

Wood. Sapwood white or pale yellow, about 2 in. thick, considered worthless and probably should be removed before the wood is used, sharply demarcated from the orange-red heartwood; heartwood very hard, heavy, and strong with a coarse grain; splits easily; rays fine but distinct; pores fairly large and surrounded by parenchyma; weight 50 to 60 lbs.

131

per cu. ft.; specific gravity 0.80 to 0.98; difficult to cut; has not been used extensively in the past; shingles have been used and have lasted more than 10 years; suitable for heavy construction and furniture; very hard and difficult to work; susceptible to termite attack and to dry rot but this may be overcome by treating with preservatives; the low resistance to cleavage or easy splitting of the wood is a definite defect, but if it is carefully handled, this should not be a serious drawback to its use.

Occurrence. Very abundant in the lowland forests, often found on moist sites and sometimes on low ridges. In the Malay States it may compose about 4 percent of the trees in the stands where it occurs and as much as 6 percent of the volume; there is about 1 tree of commercial size per acre; Malay Peninsula, Borneo, Sumatra.

FIGURE 43. *Pahudia rhomboidea*

Pahudia rhomboidea (Fig. 43)

Local Names.—Amuguan, balahiau, bagalayan, magalayao (Cagayan, Isabela); magalao (Mountain Province); bayong (Abra); apalit, pindalo (Pangasinan, Pampanga); dampul (Tarlac); bayalong (Zambales, Rizal, Laguna, Tayabas, Polillo, Marinduque, Mindoro, Masbate); barayong (Camarines, Albay, Sorsogon, Masbate, Samar, Leyte); bayong (Cebu, Surigao, Butuan, Davao); bayadgung (Surigao); bialong (Cotabato).

Habit.—Attains 30 to 40 in. in diameter and 75 to 90 ft. in height with a main stem of 35 to 45 ft. The trunk is straight, cylindrical and without buttresses.

Leaves.—Alternate, compound, 3 to 4 pairs of leaflets; leaflets are smooth, whitish underneath, ½ to 2½ in. x 2 to 4 in.

Flowers.—Borne in small terminal panicles.

Fruit.—A pod, nearly oblong, flat, 4 to 8 in. long and 2 in. wide; 1 in. in diameter, containing large black seeds.

Bark.—Creamy yellow in color, ½ in. thick; the shedding of scales leaves saucer-like depressions in the outer surface; inner bark brownish-yellow.

Wood.—Sapwood 2½ in. thick, creamy white; heartwood is light reddish-yellow when green, turning deep red with age or exposure; rays narrow and few in number; pores occur isolated and in groups, fairly evenly distributed, few in number, reddish, gummy deposit and occasionally tyloses are present; specific gravity, air-dry, 0.896; texture fine, has odor resembling that of raw beans when fresh; glossy, seasons well with very little shrinkage and warping, is easy to work and takes high finish, is very durable under all conditions. In the Philippines

134

it is considered one of the best cabinet woods and has been used for high-grade furniture, cabinet work and interior finish. In house construction it has been used for door and window frames, stairs and flooring. It is also suitable for making veneer and plywood.

Occurrence.—Very widely distributed from northern Luzon to Mindanao and Palawan in the Philippines, but is not abundant; occurs scattered on low ridges and hills near the coast and along the edges of the dipterocarp forests.

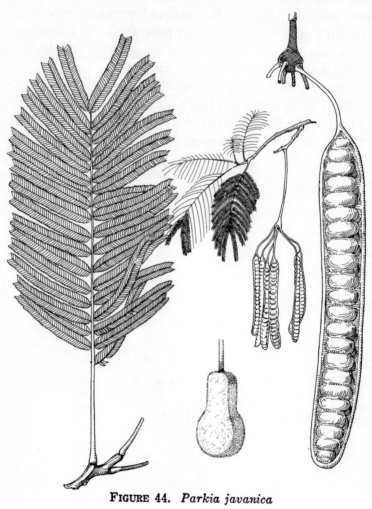

FIGURE 44. *Parkia javanica*

140. *Parkia javanica* (Fig. 44)

Local Names.—Philippines: bagin, bullisan (Mountain Province); kuyug (Pangasinan); kupang (Nueva Ecija, Bataan, Bulacan, Laguna, Rizal, Tayabas, Iloilo); maganhok (Masbate); aripa (Palawan).

Habit.—Attains a diameter of 90 in.; tall and straight with large buttresses.

Leaves.—Twice pinnately compound, with many leaflets.

Flowers.—Small, borne in heads at the ends of long stalks.

Fruit.—A flat, black, leathery stalked pod 1 to 1½ ft. long, in clusters, with several seeds in the mealy pulp.

Wood.—Sapwood, thick, white, not sharply demarcated from the light brown heartwood; rays few in number, fairly narrow, light brown, clearly visible; pores diffuse, occur singly, range from small to fairly large; parenchyma connecting vessels and at limits of growth rings, also scattered throughout the growth ring; specific gravity, air-dry, 0.285 to 0.501; grain slightly crossed, texture coarse, soft, glossy; disagreeable odor when green, without taste or odor when seasoned; seasons well and works easily, subject to blue-staining during drying; perishable when exposed in contact with the ground, and not resistant to termites; suitable for light, temporary construction; has been used for posts, fishnet floats, rafts and dugouts.

Occurrence.—Philippine Islands and New Guinea; present throughout the region.

Peltophorum pterocarpum* (P. ferrugineum, P. inerme) (Fig. 45)

Local Names. Jemerelang (Malay Peninsula); soga (Java); kadjoe djhoewok (Kangeang I., off N.E. Java); leweter (Alor or Ombay I.).

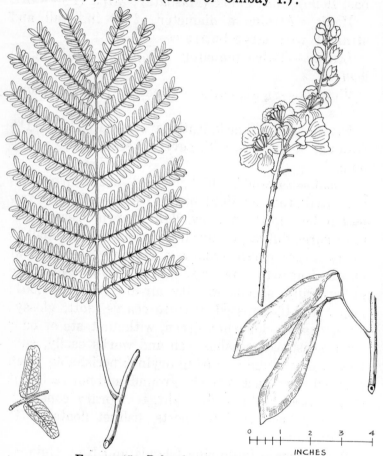

FIGURE 45. *Peltophorum pterocarpum*

138

Habit. A small to medium-sized tree attaining a diameter of 35 in. and a clear length of 18 ft.

Leaves. Bipinnately compound; when young, covered with soft tan hairs, older leaves dark green; numerous small leaflets.

Flowers. Fragrant, brilliant yellow, small, borne in panicles.

Fruit. A wine-colored pod, thin, flat, narrowly winged, borne on a short stalk; bears 1 or 2 seeds.

Wood. Sapwood whitish, sharply or gradually demarcated from the light reddish-brown heartwood; without distinct taste or odor; hard, heavy, and strong; texture medium to coarse; grain straight or wavy; easy to work or turn and finishes smoothly; weight, 47 to 63 lbs. per cu. ft.; specific gravity, air-dry, 0.75 to 1.00; considered decay resistant; glossy in appearance; has been used for furniture and small novelties.

Occurrence. Common along seashores, but may be planted inland; Burma, Malay Peninsula, Indo-China, and Siam.

FIGURE 46. *Pterocarpus indicus*

Pterocarpus indicus

Local Names. Zonnehout, angsana, sena (Malay Peninsula); asan, athan, sona, sena, hasona, sano (Sumatra); angsana (Sunda Is.); angsana, asana, sana, sana kembang (Java); sana kembang (Madura); angsana (Kangeang I., off N.E. Java and on Bali); sana (Lombok); nara (Sumbawa); ai kenawa (Sumba I.); kenaha (Solor I.); kalai (Alor or Ombay I.).

Habit. Attains 3 ft. in diameter and 80 ft. in height, with a clear length of about 25 ft.; main trunk usually short, frequently gnarled or fluted; large heavy crown; spur roots and generally wide buttresses.

Leaves. Compound, alternate; stem 3 to 5 in. long; 6 to 8 leaflets, alternate, with one terminal leaflet; petioles of leaflets 3/16 in. long, blades 1 by 1 in. to 1 by 3 in., ovate, smooth wavy margins, thin and glabrous.

Flowers. Borne in axillary racemes, 2 to 2½ in. long; yellow, fragrant.

Fruit. A winged, orbicular pod, 1½ by 3 in., containing a single seed.

Bark. Grayish-yellow to greenish-brown, about ¼ in. thick; papery scales; inner bark cream, speckled with red kino which exudes freely.

Wood. Sapwood white to pale yellow, about 2 in. thick; apparently two varieties of this species, one with white wood and the other with red wood.

White wood. Rays about 180 per in., indistinct, appear as faint lines on radial surface; pores conspicuous, 400 to 1,700 per sq. in., arranged in zones; parenchyma conspicuous, white, in wavy concentric lines, 6 to 12 per in.; specific gravity, 0.63; cuts firm.

Red wood. Rays fine, sinuous around pores, 360 per in., indistinct on radial surface; pores conspicuous, about 180 per in.; parenchyma conspicuous, white, in wavy concentric lines connecting small pores, about 70 per in.; specific gravity, 0.59; cuts soft.

A durable, soft, wood; considered fairly durable in salt water; branches take root when planted in moist ground and the natives use them for making living fences.

Occurrence. Throughout the region on coastal lowlands and on mountain slopes up to about 3,000 ft.

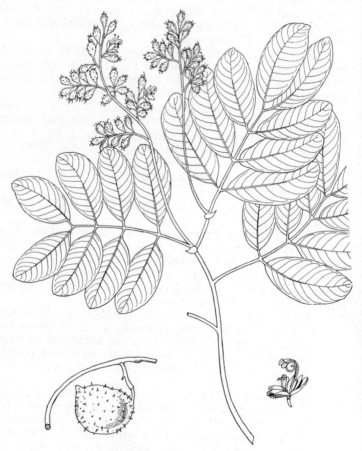

FIGURE 47. *Sindora supa*

Sindora supa (S. wallichii) (Fig. 47)

Local Names. Philippines: baloyong, tapulao (Batangas); balao (Lubong Is.); paina, parina (Tayabas, Albay); manapo, supa (Tayabas). Saputi sindo, sepetir sendok, sepah hantu (Malay Peninsula); petir (Rhio Archipelago, south of Singapore Strait); sepoetih sendok (Malacca); tamparhantoe (S.E. Sumatra, Palembang).

Habit. Attains a diameter of 71 in. and develops a main stem of 30 to 35 ft. in length; tall and straight, with little taper and only small buttresses.

Leaves. Alternate, compound, with 3 or 4 pairs of leaflets; smooth and leathery, oblong, 1 by 3 in., with fine hairs below.

Flowers. Small, numerous, yellowish-brown or tinted with red, borne in axillary panicles, 6 to 8 in. long.

Fruit. A flat, dry, oblong pod, 2 by 3 in., with short spines, containing 1 or 2 flat, black or yellow seeds.

Bark. Thick, 3½ to 5 in., brown or almost black, sheds large scales which expose pink patches beneath.

Wood. Sapwood 4 in. thick, pinkish, distinctly demarcated from yellow-red heartwood; heartwood turns chestnut brown with exposure; rays narrow, few, light colored but distinctly visible; pores in groups of 2 or 3, evenly distributed, small, with occasional reddish gummy deposits; cross-grained; texture fine; glossy in appearance and without distinctive taste or odor; moderately hard; specific gravity, air-dry, 0.83; seasons slowly, but with little difficulty; may be hard to work with ordinary tools, but takes a high finish; durable in interior work but only moderately resistant to decay when exposed; has been used for high grade furniture and cabinet work, in house construction for flooring, door and window frames and for picture frames, novelties, radio cabinets and piano cases.

Occurrence. Malay Peninsula; Philippines, common on Luzon, Mindoro, Tayabas and Camarines; usually found near seashores back of mangrove swamps in forests of low altitudes; is not abundant although fairly uniformly distributed; other species of this genus present in the Moluccas, Celebes, Sumatra and Borneo.

Linaceae

(Flax Family)

Woody and herbaceous plants, rarely trees, distributed widely throughout tropical and temperate zones. Leaves without petioles, alternate or opposite; flowers regular, sepals and petals three to five; fruit six- to ten-celled with one seed in each cell. Plants usually yield adhesives and fibers.

Ixonanthes reticulata (Fig. 48)

Local Names. Jinjangong, jenjagong, jejagong, sakit hudang, pagar anak (Malay Peninsula).

Habit. A small tree, attains about 20 ft. in height.

Leaves. Stiff, leathery, dark green, and shiny, elliptical, 2 by 3½ in. to 3 by 5 in.; petioles 1 in. long.

Flowers. About ¼ in. long, borne in short cymes.

Fruit. An oblong capsule, 1½ to 2 in. long, woody.

Occurrence. Malay Peninsula, Borneo; allied species present in Indo-China, Hainan, and Southern China.

FLOWER

$\frac{2\frac{1}{2}}{1}$

FRUIT

0 1 2 3
INCHES

FIGURE 48. *Ixonanthes reticulata*

145

Rutaceae

(Rue Family)

146. Trees, shrubs and some herbs dispersed chiefly in the warm countries of the eastern hemisphere, where the plants are characterized by pinnate or much divided leaves with small glands containing aromatic oil. It includes the citrus-bearing fruits and the satinwoods of commerce of both hemispheres.

FIGURE 49. —*Flindersia amboinensis.*

Flindersia macrocarpa (*see* Fig. 49 for similar species)

Local Names.—Zizanu (Laruni).

Habit.—Attains 3 ft. in diameter and 100 ft. in height and with 70 ft. of clear length; without buttresses.

Leaves.—Compound, alternate, 9 in. long; leaflets opposite, 4 pairs and a terminal one; leaflet petiole ¼ in. long; blade 2 by 3 to 8 in., lanceolate, midrib prominent yellow, smooth, leathery.

Fruit.—Green, 9 in. long, with stout spines ½ in. long; borne 2 to 3 on stout stalk 8 in. long; opens at maturity into 5 canoe-shaped segments, each with numerous winged seeds.

Bark.—Gray-brown, ⅜ in. thick, faintly longitudinally lined, fibrous; inner bark yellow-brown and streaked with yellow.

Wood.—White to yellow; sapwood not demarcated from heartwood; rays 120 to 140 per in., yellow, appear as yellow lines on radial surface; pores 3,000 to 6,000 per sq. in., scattered pores between narrow zones of crowded pores; specific gravity 0.754; a hard wood.

Occurence.—New Guinea and Moluccas; large trees of the rain forest, frequent to common on well-drained soils from lowlands high in mountains; this is one of several tree species in the genus, all of which are good timber trees.

Simarubaceae

(Quassia Family)

148. Trees and shrubs confined chiefly to the warmer parts of the northern hemisphere. Leaves are alternate, simple or pinnately compound. Fruit is a drupe, berry, capsule or samara. Bark is usually very bitter. Plants afford essential and fatty oils, bitter principles and some doubtful medicinal properties. The quassia wood of commerce is produced by this family.

FIGURE 50. —*Ailanthus blancoi*

Ailanthus philippensis (see **Fig. 50** for similar species)

Local Names.—Kulaike (Rizal); malakameas (Laguna); malaadusa (Tayabas); kalauag (Camarines); bangloi (Iloilo); empau, maramaranggo (Palawan).

Habit.—A medium sized tree attaining 30 in. in diameter and with 30 ft. of clear length; trunk is straight and cylindrical.

Leaves.—Pinnately compound, alternate, 20 to 30 in. long.

Flowers.—Yellow, without odor.

Fruit.—Dry nonopening, winged, nearly oblong, about 2 in. long.

Wood.—Sapwood not sharply demarcated from the yellow to buff heartwood; growth rings not distinct; rays narrow to fairly broad, lighter in color than surrounding tissue; pores isolated and in groups, diffuse, surrounded with narrow ring of parenchyma, occasional tyloses present; specific gravity, air-dry, 0.490; straight grained, coarse textured, lustrous; without pronounced odor, slightly bitter taste; seasons well without warping or checking but is susceptible to blue-staining; is easy to work and to finish, not durable and easily damaged by fungi and insects. It has been used for making wooden shoes, boxes, match boxes, spear handles, canoes and for other purposes for which a soft, light wood is required.

Occurrence.—Confined to Luzon, Iloilo and Palawan in the Philippines; the supply is very limited. Other species of the genus occur in the Philippines, and in Celebes, Moluccas and New Guinea.

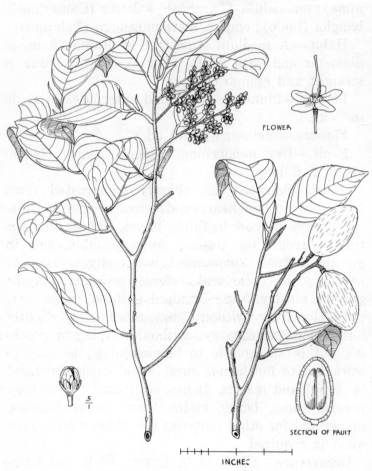

FLOWER

SECTION OF FRUIT

INCHES

FIGURE 51. *Irvingia malayana*

Irvingia malayana (Fig. 51)

Local Names. Pauh kijang, paoeh kidjang, kebayang kumus, merlang (Malay Peninsula); poeh bajan, paoeh roesoe, paoeh menteh, kalek karsik (Sumatra); kajoe bongin, sepah (West Borneo).

Habit. Attains 150 ft. in height, often with 80 ft. of clear length; large buttresses and a large crown.

Leaves. Simple, ovate or elliptical, leathery, 2 in. by 3½ in. to 2½ in. by 6 in.; petioles ½ in. long.

Flowers. Borne in axillary and terminal panicles which are 2 to 4 in. long; flowers ¼ in. wide, dark green.

Fruit. Ovate and flattened, 2 in. long, green with an orange-colored fibrous pulp, resembles a mango.

Occurrence. Malay Peninsula; allied species present in Indo-China.

Burseraceae

(Torchwood or Myrrh Family)

150. Tropical woody plants, mostly unarmed trees and shrubs rich in aromatic gum-resins containing essential oils; the resins have been known and used since ancient times; leaves compound, with transparent dots. Valuable woods are afforded by the species of a few genera, particularly *Canarium*, which occur throughout Indian Archipelago and the South Pacific islands.

Canarium commune (Fig. 52)

Local Names. Java almond tree; Java almond, kanari, kenari (Malay Peninsula); kanari (Sunda Islands); kenari (Java); kanaleh, konari (Madura); kanari (Sumbawa); kodja (Flores I.).

Habit. A large tree; extremities of branches tawny.

Leaves. Compound, 9 to 18 in. long; leaflets 7 to 9, ovate to elliptical, smooth, 1 by 4 in. to 2 by 6 in.; petioles ½ to 1 in. long.

Flowers. About ¼ in. long, borne in terminal spreading panicles.

Fruit. An ellipsoidal drupe with a 1- to 3-celled stone or pit.

Bark. The resinous exudate has the same properties as balsam of copaiba, and is used medicinally.

Wood. Wood tan to reddish-brown; grain crossed or wavy, texture fine; moderately soft, difficult to saw; growth rings indistinct; pores isolated and in groups, small and diffuse; parenchyma surrounding the pores narrow, inconspicuous; rays few, and may contain horizontal resin ducts; suitable for temporary construction, boxes, crates, and veneer.

Occurrence. Malay Peninsula; there are many other species of the genus present from Burma to Southeast China and the Malay Archipelago.

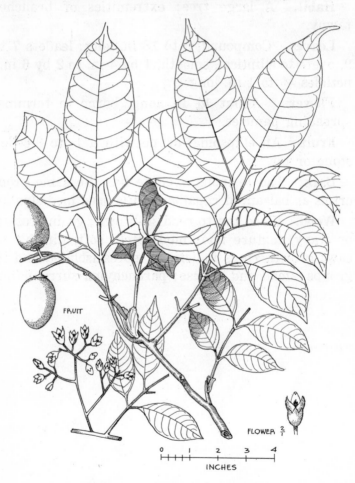

FRUIT

FLOWER $\frac{2}{1}$

0 1 2 3 4
INCHES

FIGURE 52. *Canarium commune*

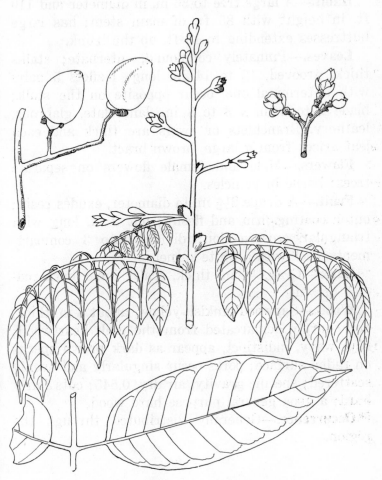

FIGURE 53.—*Canarium mehenbetnene.*

Canarium grandistipulatum (see **Fig. 53** for similar species)

Local Names.—Mahei (Vailala, New Guinea).

Habit.—A large tree to 36 in. in diameter and 110 ft. in height with 85 ft. of main stem; has large buttresses extending to 15 ft. up the trunk.

Leaves.—Pinnately compound, alternate; stalks thick, grooved, 12 to 14 in. long; leaflets 5 pairs with a terminal one, occur opposite on the stalk; blade 2 to 4 in. x 3 to 8 in., lanceolate, glabrous, leathery. Branchlets or twigs are thick and each leaf arises from a large, brown bract.

Flowers.—Male and female flowers on separate trees; borne in panicles.

Fruit.—A drupe 2½ in. in diameter, exudes resin; outer coating firm and fleshy; nut 2 in. long with triangular cross-section; divides into 3 compartments, each with a white kernel.

Bark.—Gray, ¼ in. thick, scaly; inner bark reddish-brown.

Wood.—Sapwood pinkish-yellow, about 3 in. thick, not sharply demarcated from the pink heartwood; rays wavy, indistinct, appear as dark brown specks on radial surface; pores occur singularly and evenly scattered; specific gravity, air dry, 0.545; cuts fairly hard; a good general purpose hard wood.

Occurrence.—Generally distributed through the region.

FIGURE 54.—*Canarium villosum*

159

Canarium lineistipulum (see **Fig. 54** for similar species)

Local Names.—Sisera (Buna), wairo (Vailala), nuri (Evara).

Habit.—Attains 2½ ft. in diameter and develops 60 ft. of clear length, buttressed.

Leaves.—Pinnately compound, alternate; 9 to 14 in. overall; 4 to 5 pairs opposite leaflets; leaflet petiole with fine hairs, ⅜ in. long; blade 2 by 7 in., obovate.

Flowers.—In panicles, cream colored.

Fruit.—A berry, ⅜ in. in diameter; the seed is eaten by the natives and Europeans.

Bark.—Yellow-brown, with papery scales; inner bark salmon-pink.

Wood.—Sapwood pale yellow not clearly demarcated from pink-yellow heartwood; rays 170 per in., yellow, sinuous; pores conspicuous, 4,000 to 5,000 per sq. in., evenly distributed; straight grained; specific gravity 0.465 to 0.530; cuts firm; a medium soft wood.

Occurrence.—Lowlands and lower slopes, Kumusi River, Northern Division, New Guinea; this is one of many timber trees in this genus; the Nali-nut tree of the Solomons also belongs to this genus.

Canarium moluense

Habit.—Attains 30 in. in diameter, 110 ft. in height with 80 ft. of main stem; without buttresses.

Leaves.—Pinnately compound, alternate; stalk 5 in. long is swollen at the base to 1/4 in. in diameter; leaflets 2 pairs and a terminal one, rarely three pairs; leaflets opposite, blade 2 to 5 in. x 3 to 7 in., sharply pointed at apex, leathery, midribs and veins yellow and very prominent; slightly hairy on lower side.

Flowers.—Borne in axillary panicles, 6 to 9 in. long.

Fruit.—A drupe, triangular in cross-section, with 1 to 3 cells but only one seed.

Bark.—Gray with yellow blotches, 1/4 in. thick; smooth, except for numerous corky pustules; inner bark yellowish-brown; exudes fragrant resin.

Wood.—Wood white to yellowish, sapwood not sharply demarcated from heartwood; rays reddish-brown, broken, very sinuous and around pores, appear as specks on the radial surface; pores occur singularly; specific gravity, air-dry, 0.594; cuts firm to hard; a straight grained, medium hard wood.

Occurrence.—New Guinea, known to occur on Hydrographer's Range; throughout the Moluccas and Celebes.

Meliaceae

(Chinaberry Family)

154. This family contains about 50 genera and over 1,000 species. The leaves are pinnately compound, alternate, or opposite. The flowers are small and borne in panicles, and the fruit varies from a berry to a dry capsule with many seeds. The bark is dry and astringent. The Spanish cedar is produced by *Cedrela* and mahogany by *Swietenia* in the western hemisphere.

FIGURE 56. —*Cedrela toona*

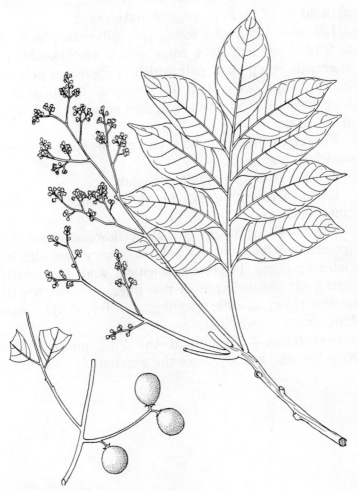

FIGURE 55. —*Aglaia llanosiana*

Aglaia elaeagnoidea (see **Fig. 55** for similar species).

Local Names.—Uva (Suku, New Guinea).

Habit.—A medium size tree to 30 in. in diameter with 30 ft. of main stem; not buttressed.

Leaves.—Pinnately compound, alternate; stalk 7 to 9 in. long; leaflets 4 pairs with a terminal leaflet alternate except last pair which is opposite; petioles ¼ in. long, blade 3 x 5 in., ovate to lanceolate, sharply pointed at apex, margins smooth; thin, reddish-brown.

Flowers.—Small, yellow, borne in open axillary panicles, fragrant.

Fruit.—A drupe, small, globular.

Bark.—Greenish-gray, to ½ in. thick, smooth; inner bark yellow.

Wood.—Wood white to pale yellow, sapwood not demarcated from heartwood; rays very fine and indistinct; pores large, conspicuous and irregularly scattered; parenchyma in fine lines at right angles to the rays; specific gravity, air dry, 0.674; cuts firm, grain interlocked.

Occurrence.—Throughout the Philippines and in New Guinea, mainly near the seashore.

Aglai sapindina

Local Names.—Digisi (Buna), zigisi (Binandele); also pronounced sigisi and jigisi.

Habit.—Attains 30 in. in diameter and with 60 ft. of main stem; has medium sized buttresses extending to 7 ft. up the trunk.

Leaves.—Pinnately compound, alternate; stalk 8 in. to 18 in. long; leaflets opposite, 6 to 7 pairs and with or without a terminal leaflet; blade 2 by 6 in., elliptical, sharply pointed, thin, margin finely toothed.

Flowers.—Borne in axillary panicles about 6 in. long. Flowers are very small, white and fragrant.

Fruit.—Globose, ½ in. in diameter, green, speckled with brown, bearing 2 to 4 seeds.

Bark.—Greenish-brown, ½ in. thick, has linear lines or flat ridges; inner bark light brown streaked with yellow.

Wood.—Pale yellow to pink in color, sapwood not sharply demarcated from heartwood; rays coarse, brown, sinuous around pores, appear as faint lines on radial surface; parenchyma conspicuous in lines thicker than the rays, in zigzag arrangement; specific gravity, air-dry, 0.530; cuts very soft.

Occurrence.—Occurs in Buna district, Sangara, and throughout the plains country, New Guinea.

Cedrela toona (C. febrifuga) (Fig. 56)

Local Names. New Guinea: red cedar, mafus (Lower Markham Valley); epi (Suku); kapere (Vailala); mufus (Yalu). Suntang putch, ingoe, soeren (Malay Peninsula); ki beureum, soeren (Sunda Is.); laoet, redani, soeren (Java); soren (Madura); horeni, linoe (Sumba).

Habit. Attains 5 ft. in diameter and 120 ft. in height with 80 ft. clear length; thick spur buttresses.

Leaves. Pinnately compound, alternate, deciduous, 15 to 24 in. long; petiole 12 to 19 in. long; leaflets alternate, 6 to 10 pairs, ovate, 2 by 4 to 3 by 5 in., membranous, glabrous.

Flowers. Borne in long loose panicles, 12 to 18 in. long; flowers ¼ in. in diameter.

Fruit. An ellipsoidal capsule, 1 in. long, containing many winged seeds, ½ to ¾ in. long.

Bark. About ½ in. thick, rough, scaly, deep fissured, reddish- or grayish-brown; inner bark red.

Wood. Sapwood 1 in. thick, white or pale yellow-brown; heartwood cedar-brown; rays narrow, few, conspicuous only on radial surface; growth rings marked by rows of large pores; pores large in early wood and small in late wood, occasionally filled with black gummy deposits; parenchyma red, surrounding pores and in straight lines, finer than rays, also terminal; specific gravity 0.739; fragrant; cuts soft and wooly; resistant to termites; a good cigar box wood, suitable for house construction, furniture, cabinet work, carving, planking, and interior finish.

Occurrence. Throughout the region but not abundant in any one place; favors deep well-drained soils of alluvial flats, and low ridges and mountain slopes; extends from coastal lowlands to about 5,000 ft.; allied species present in Indo-China, Hainan, Borneo and southern China.

166

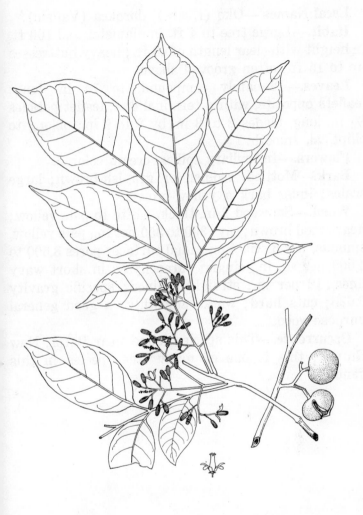

FIGURE 57. —*Dysoxylum arborescens.*

Dysoxylum pettigrewianum (see Fig. 57 for similar species)

Local Names.—Oko (Evara), dorokea (Vailala).

Habit.—Large tree to 4 ft. in diameter and 100 ft. in height with clear length of 60 ft.; heavy buttresses up to 15 ft., often grooved above.

Leaves.—Pinnately compound, to 14 in. long; leaflets opposite, with a terminal one; leaflet petioles $\frac{1}{2}$ in. long, blades 2 to 3 in. by 3 to 9 in., oblong to elliptical, smooth.

Flowers.—In axillary spikes, cream colored.

Bark.—Mottled, reddish or grayish-brown; large scales; inner bark a yellow-brown.

Wood.—Sapwood 2 in. thick, white to pale yellow; heartwood brown; rays 300 to 350 per in., pale yellow, sinuous, not distinct on radial surface; pores 3,500 to 4,000 per sq. in., single; parenchyma in short wavy lines, 12 per in.; straight-grained; specific gravity 0.625; cuts hard; works smoothly; a good general purpose wood.

Occurrence.—This species found near Baroi; New Guinea; this is one of many tree species in this genus.

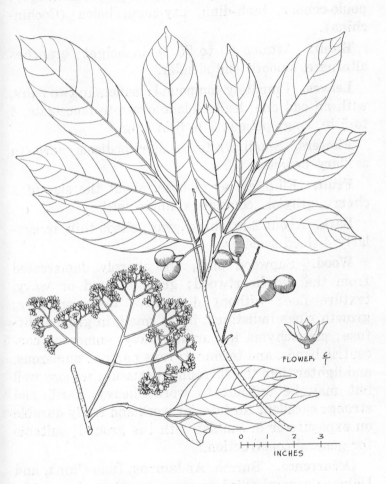

FLOWER $\frac{6}{1}$

0 1 2 3
INCHES

FIGURE 58. *Walsura robusta*

Walsura robusta (Fig. 58)

Local Names. Phu-guoe, sandek-prey (Camboge) ; poulo-condor, binh-dinh, cay-cong, baloa (Cochinchina).

Habit. Attains 60 to 75 ft. in height; branches alternate, smooth and slender.

Leaves. Pinnately compound; leaflets in two pairs, with an odd one; leaflet blade ovate to lanceolate, 4 to 5 in. long; petiole, 3 to 5 in long.

Flowers. Small, white, on short pedicels; borne in axillary panicles.

Fruit. Elliptical or globose, about the size of a cherry, grayish, contains a single seed.

Bark. About 2 in. thick, gray; sheds thin, irregularly 4-sided scales.

Wood. Sapwood pink, not sharply demarcated from the red heartwood; grain crossed or wavy, texture fine; without distinctive taste or odor; growth rings indistinct; pores small, in groups, diffuse; parenchyma in narrow, wavy, numerous concentric bands, and terminal; rays narrow, numerous, and lighter than the surrounding tissue; seasons well but may be difficult to work; heavy, hard, and strong; excellent for interior work and fairly durable on exposure or in contact with the ground; suitable for general construction.

Occurrence. Burma, Andamans, Indo-China, and Hainan; several allied species present in the region.

FIGURE 59. –*Xylocarpus granatum.*

Xylocarpus granatum (Carapa moluccensis)
(Fig. 59)

Local Names.—Cannon-ball tree, apple mangrove (Australia), Kasi-Kasi (Eastern Papua), wagua (Tufi), laure (Buna), apura (Vailala), kairu (Motu), miri, niri (Malayan); pamoeli, kabaoe, giliki gota (Halmahera).

Habit.—A small to medium sized tree, 20 in. diameter and 60 ft. in height; may have small buttresses.

Leaves.—Pinnately compound, alternate 2 to 4 in. overall; 2 pairs opposite leaflets, obovate or elliptical, distinct venation, somewhat leathery; light brown twigs.

Fruit.—Globose, 7½ in. in diameter; rind ¼ in. thick, green, smooth, with brown markings, opens in four parts, inside pink; about 20 seeds, 1 by 1¾, grouped in 5's, one group in each quarter seeds are water disseminated.

Bark.—Thin, about 1/16 in., yellow-brown, flakes off in patches resembling sycamore.

Wood.—Yellow to red; sapwood not demarcated from heartwood; rays 230 per in., yellow, appear as specks on radial surface; pores, 3,200 to 5,700 per sq. in.; parenchyma in thin lines, about 6 per in.; grain scarcely visible; specific gravity, 0.610; cuts hard; tough; durable; has reputation for resistance to teredo; used for salt water piling in eastern Papua; has also been used for furniture.

Occurrence.—Throughout the region; common on the landward side of the mangrove forests toward higher ground; never found inland.

Euphorbiaceae

(Spurge Family)

Trees, shrubs, and herbs with acrid or often milky, purgative, or poisonous juice. Leaves are alternate or opposite, entire and dentate, or lobed. Plants of this family are widely distributed over tropical and temperate regions of both hemispheres. Fruit is usually capsular, sometimes drupaceous, and commonly three-celled, as in the case of the castor-oil plant. Some species yield starch, fatty and essential oils, rubber, dyes, and valuable woods.

Trees, shrubs, and herbs with watery or milky juice. Leaves are alternate or opposite, entire and simple or palmately lobed or compound. Flowers small, unisexual, monoecious or dioecious.

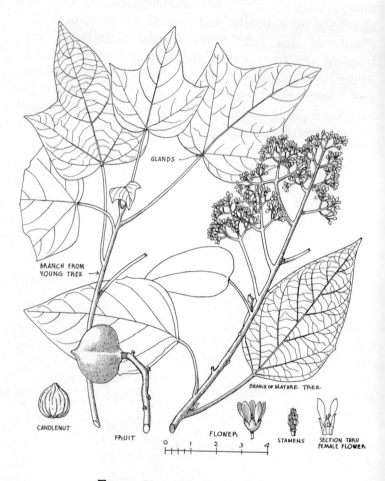

GLANDS

BRANCH FROM
YOUNG TREE

BRANCH OF MATURE TREE

CANDLENUT

FRUIT

0 1 2 3 4

FLOWER

STAMENS

SECTION THRU
FEMALE FLOWER

FIGURE 60. *Aleurites moluccana*

174

Aleurites moluccana (Fig. 60)

Local Names. Bancoulier, belgaum walnut, candlenut tree; buah keras, kemiri, kembiri, camiri nut, candle nut, Singapore nut (Malay Peninsula); kereh, kemili, kembiri, gambiri, boewah kareh, kemiling (Sumatra); moentjang (Sunda Is.); peridjah, kemiling, keminting (Borneo); derekan, pidekan, kemiri (Java); kamere (Madura); derekan, kemeri, tingkih (Bali); lekong, miri (Lombok); kaleli (Sumbawa); kawiloe (Sumba); kamieh (Solor); kamiri (Pantar).

Habit. Attains 15 to 20 in. in diameter and 60 ft. in height.

Leaves. Ovate or lanceolate, 2½ by 3 in. to 3 by 6 in., some leaves tri-lobed and 8 in. wide by 9 in. long; petioles 2½ to 6 in. long.

Flowers. Numerous, white, small; borne in dense panicles which are 4 in. long.

Fruit. Globose, fleshy, olive-colored, 2 to 2½ in. long, contains 1 or 2 seeds which have a bony covering and oily kernel.

Wood. Light tan in color; texture fine to coarse; medium weight and fairly soft; growth rings indistinct; pores isolated and in groups, diffuse, small to fairly large; parenchyma inconspicuous, in concentric bands, very narrow and numerous; rays narrow; has been used for making matches and wooden shoes.

Occurrence. Common, both wild and planted; Malay Peninsula and Archipelago.

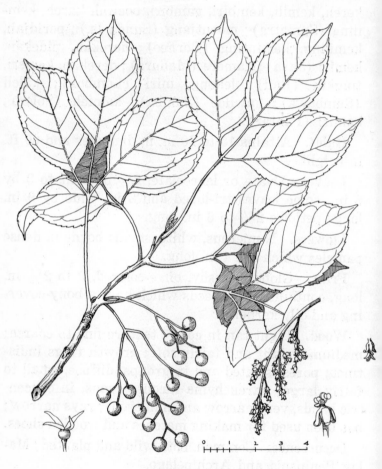

FIGURE 61. *Bischofia javanica*

Bischofia javanica (Fig. 61)

Local Names. Gerondjing (Malayan) ; tingkeum, singkam, bintoengan (Sumatra) ; gadog; ki mahoeng (Sunda Is.) ; gintoeng (Java).

Habit. Attains 50 in. in diameter and 30 to 40 ft. in height, but the main trunk is very short, usually with a clear length of about 25 ft.; generally straight and without buttresses.

Leaves. Compound on a petiole 2 to 6 in. long; leaflets from ovate to lanceolate, usually three; petioles very short.

Flowers. Green, borne in axillary panicles; female flowers small, male ones minute.

Fruit. A globular drupe, about the size of a pea, smooth, juicy, bluish-black.

Bark. Smooth, dark gray.

Wood. Sapwood light red, 1 to 2 in. thick, demarcated from the brownish-red heartwood; growth rings not distinct but may be discerned by dark bands of dense late wood; pores in groups of 2 to 3, quite small, few to numerous, dark red tyloses present; wood parenchyma diffuse; rays fairly broad, numerous, straight, dark in color; grain crossed, texture moderately fine; dull in appearance, without characteristic taste or odor; heavy and hard; specific gravity, air-dry, 0.814; must be carefully seasoned to avoid warping and checking; easy to work, durable in interior work but not durable when exposed or in contact with the ground; suitable for general construction when protected.

177

Occurrence. Common in the forests along streams and hill savannahs at low and medium altitudes, to about 2,000-ft. elevation; obtainable in small quantities, but has seldom been cut for timber in the past; present throughout the region.

Endospermum formicarum.

Local Names.—Kerea (Suku, New Guinea).

Habit.—Attains 30 in. in diameter with 70 ft. of main stem; narrow buttresses up to 8 ft.

Leaves.—Simple, alternate; petiole to 5½ in. long; blade to 8 in. in diameter, smooth, leathery.

Flowers.—Borne in axillary panicles 6 in. long.

Fruit.—A green, hairy berry, contains 1 seed.

Bark.—Smooth, gray-brown, ½ in. thick; inner bark streaked with white and orange.

Wood.—White to yellow, sapwood not sharply demarcated from heartwood; rays appear as wavy lines on the radial surface; pores irregularly scattered or in short chains; parenchyma in very fine lines connecting the rays; specific gravity, air-dry, 0.433; cuts soft; suitable for interior work, has an attractive grain on the radial surface.

Occurrence.—New Guinea at Vanapa, Veimauri and Aroa.

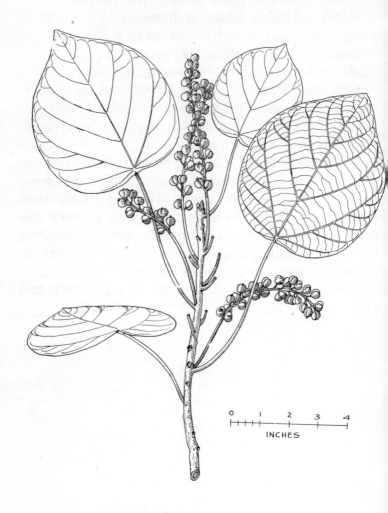

FIGURE 62. *Endospermum malaccense*

Endospermum malaccense (Fig. 62)

Local Names. Bebaru, bukit, baru bukit, kadjoe radja, kajoe semoet, bembulan, marabulan, mahang puteh, membulan, medang kelabu, sendok-sendok, sesundo (Malay Peninsula).

Habit. Attains 24 in. in diameter and 80 ft. in height; branchlets are stout.

Leaves. Ovate, broad at base, blade 3½ by 4½ in. to 4½ by 5 in.; petioles 2 in. long.

Flowers. Yellow, without peduncles, very fragrant.

Fruit. Green, globose, 0.2 in. in diameter.

Bark. Smooth, gray.

Wood. Light buff, may have a red tint; texture fine to fairly coarse, medium weight and hardness; growth rings generally indistinct; pores isolated and in groups, diffuse, small; parenchyma inconspicuous; rays narrow; has been used for making match sticks and boxes, veneer, wooden shoes; suitable for all general construction for which a soft, light wood is required; not resistant to either insects or fungi unless treated with preservatives.

Occurrence. Common in low-lying forests; Malay Peninsula; allied species present in the Archipelago.

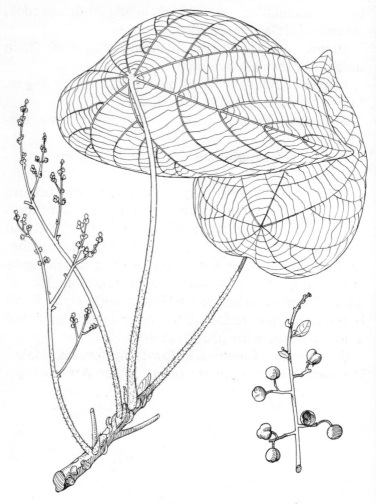

FIGURE 63.—*Endospermum peltatum*

Endospermum peltatum (Fig. 63)

Local Names.—Bau-bau (Cagayan) ; badyana (Ilocos Sur) ; ginabang (Mountain Province) ; mulang (Zambales) ; binuang (Nueva Ecija, Bulacan, Bataan, Rizal, Laguna, Tabayas) ; gubas, kalinkoi, kalukoi (Bataan) ; bolauisan, indang, malasabon (Laguna) ; kabal (Tagalog) ; anilang, luktub (Tayabas) ; biliu-ang (Sorsogon, Albay) ; biluang (Camarines, Mindoro) ; libas (Camarines) ; malatagon, luktob (Mindoro) ; lubang, taawa (Palawan) ; salingobod (Misamis) ; bai-ang (Agusan) ; malibukbuk (Lanao, Cotabato) ; megabong (Cotabato).

Habit.—A large tree, to 40 in. in diameter, 75 to 100 ft. tall and with 25 to 35 ft. of main stem; trunk generally straight without large buttresses.

Leaves.—Alternate, simple and hairy, ovate or heart-shaped, 5 to 8 in. long, entire, crowned at ends of the branchlets.

Flowers.—Borne in panicles; male flowers white, numerous, panicles 4 to 8 in. long; female flowers few, panicles 10 in. long.

Fruit.—Ovoid, glabrous, ½ in. long, outer layer somewhat fleshy, enclosing the seed.

Bark.—Light gray with an orange tinge; ¼ to ½ in. thick, inner bark is golden yellow and has a disagreeable odor.

Wood.—Sapwood not sharply demarcated from the tan to pale orange-yellow heartwood; rays narrow, few in number; pores mostly in groups of 2 to 3, small to large; parenchyma in narrow bands, separated from the pores, diffuse, growth rings indistinct; specific gravity air-dry 0.335 to 0.460, average 0.4000; grain is straight, texture coarse, without distinct taste or odor, light, soft and weak, sus-

183

ceptible to blue-staining, works easily, readily attacked by insects and is not resistant to decay; has been used for match sticks and match boxes, veneer, wooden shoes, boxes, and other purposes for which a soft light wood is required.

Occurrence.—Philippines; widely distributed on Luzon, Mindoro and Mindanao in virgin forests at low and medium altitudes; obtainable only in small quantities. Other species in this genus are present to New Guinea.

GLANDS

0 1 2 3 4
INCHES

FIGURE 64. *Sapium baccatum*

185

Sapium baccatum (Fig. 64)

Local Names. Ludai pelandok, ludai, mayang, memaya, rulus, mamas-mamas pelandok, kayu rulus (Malay Peninsula) ; banai (Simaloe I. off N.W. Sumatra) ; bedi, boedi, ludahi (S.E. Sumatra, Palembang).

Habit. A large tree.

Leaves. Oblong to ovate, smooth margins, 2 by 3 in. to 3 by 7 in.; petioles 1 to 2 in. long.

Flowers. Small, with very short pedicels, borne in spreading panicles which are about 5 in. long.

Fruit. Green, fleshy, ½ in. in diameter.

Wood. White or yellowish, light and soft; works easily but may be "woolly"; not resistant to either insects or fungi; susceptible to blue-staining during drying; suitable for emergency construction only, interior work, and boxes.

Occurrence. Malay Peninsula, Sumatra,. Indo-China.

Anacardiaceae

(Cashew Family)

Trees and shrubs distributed throughout the warmer parts of the world. Many of the more important species yield valuable products such as tannin, dyestuffs, gums, resins, fatty oils, fruits, nuts, and woods. The mango tree *(Mangifera indica)* affords one of the most valuable tropical fruits. The trees of some genera such as *Semecarpus, Rhus, Campnosperma, Gluta, Swintonia,* and some species of *Mangifera* produce sap which is a contact poison causing skin eruptions similar to those due to poison ivy and poison oak, since the active principle is the same in all.

FIGURE 65. *Buchanania arbu. escens*

Buchanania arborescens

Local Names. Njatoh boenga, otak oedang, teren-
tang ajam (Malayan); rawa-rawa pipit (S. E. Borneo); popohan, reungas manoek (Sunda Is.); popohan,
getasan (Java); araka, ganga, kamung, palang, pap-
pagan (Cagayan); pavan (Ilocos Norte); rangas (Cagayan, Ilocos Norte, Pangasinan); langlanges (Ilocos
Sur); kanteng (Abra, Mountain Province); arenges
(Isabela); palankomog, uyok (Mountain Province);
havan (Nueva Vizcaya); bisal, bolowan, boroan, bu-
luan, kaming, pakaran rangas (Pangasinan); baling-
hai (Zambales); balinghasai (Nueva Ecija, Tarlac,
Bulacan, Bataan, Rizal, Laguna, Batangas, Cavite,
Tayabas, Mindoro, Cotabato, Davao, Zamboanga);
kimiling, kaming, kaning (Tarlac, Zambales, Bataan); alitagtag, balitagtag (Tayabas, Camarines);
bagulibas, balansai, balansi, balinsood, unkan (Mindoro); balayohot, balihod, balingahood, balitangtang,
hongas, maguliok, malaligas na lalake (Tayabas);
balinghasai, bahai-uud (Tagalog); balehod, upong-
upong, kalampuso (Camarines); tagangtang (Ticao);
ana-an, kalantang, karangtang, malapog (Palawan);
butubutu (Cebu); anegas (Negros Occidental); anam, an-an (Mindoro, Iloilo, Surigao); lagindingan
(Cotabato); balanga (Guimaras); maumanga (Davao); balunug, dilaan, manbaluno, mangapuli (Sulu).

Habit. A medium-sized tree to 30 in. in diameter
and with a main stem of 25 to 35 ft. in length; has
small buttresses.

Leaves. Simple, alternate, bunched at ends of
rather stout twigs; 1 by 5 in. to 4 by 15 in.

Flowers. Small, white, numerous, borne in terminal and axillary panicles.

Fruit. A small compressed drupe containing a
single seed; a black varnish is obtained from it.

Bark. Four to 5 in. thick, smooth, may have many
small knobs, brownish in color, with grayish-yellow
tinge; inner bark red.

Wood. Sapwood 2 to 3 in. thick, light in color, not
sharply demarcated from the light gray heartwood;
rays narrow, numerous, reddish, and darker than surrounding tissue, straight, or slightly wavy; pores isolated, in groups of 2 to 3, evenly distributed, small,

without deposits; specific gravity, air-dry, 0.630; grain straight or slightly crossed; texture fine; without distinctive taste or odor; glossy; moderately strong; seasons well, works easily and takes a high finish; not resistant to insect attack and not durable when exposed or in contact with the ground; is suitable for light construction, interior finish, furniture, household implements and cigar boxes.

Occurrence. Common at low and medium altitudes in the second growth forests, but is not abundant; Philippines, Burma, Malay Peninsula, Malay Archipelago, Siam, and Indo-China.

FIGURE 66.—*Campnosperma montana.*

Campnosperma brevipetiolata (see Fig. 66 for similar species)

Local Names.—Siruga (Buna), siluya (Middle Sepik, Onitatandi), kwata (Lower Sepik), singawa (Rabaul).

Habit.—A large tree, to 3½ ft. in diameter and 80 ft. of clear length; heavy buttresses up to 8 ft.

Leaves.—Simple, crowded at ends of branches, 7 by 22 in., oblanceolate, stiff, smooth; midrib and veins yellow.

Fruit.—A round, purple drupe, with flattened ovoid green seed; borne in axillary panicles 15 in. long.

Bark.—¼ in. thick, thin papery scales; inner bark streaked with cream and yellow; sap may cause skin irritation similar to poison ivy and treatment is the same.

Wood.—Sapwood cream color, merges with pinkish-yellow heartwood; rays 210 per in., brown sinuous appear as fine lines and rectangles on radial surface; pores 18,000 per sq. in., evenly distributed; straight grained; cuts firm; turns marine-brown when dry; specific gravity 0.706; suitable for siding and sheathing; principal canoe-log tree of eastern Papua; yields a yellow oil.

Occurrence.—Papua, New Guinea; in swamps, alluvial flats, low ridges.

FIGURE 67.—*Dracontomelum sylvestre.*

Dracontomelum mangiferum (see Fig. 67 for similar species)

Local Names.—Onomba (Buna, Binendele), lup (New Britain), damoni (Motu), ava (Vailala), dorea (Evara).

Habit.—A large tree, to 3½ ft. in diameter and 120 ft. in height, with very long, large buttresses—probably the strongest buttressed tree in Papua.

Leaves.—Pinnately compound, alternate, leaflets alternate; blade 2 to 6 in. by 1 to 2 in., smooth margins, thin, smooth.

Bark.—¼ in. thick, mottled brown and olive; scaly but bark peels in irregular patches leaving smooth surface which is pale green; inner bark pale yellow.

Wood.—Sapwood 4 in. thick, pale yellow; heartwood walnut brown; rays 200 per in., inconspicuous; pores conspicuous, 500 per sq. in., contain dark deposit, irregularly scattered; grain resembles walnut; cuts hard; specific gravity 0.753; has been cut commercially in Papua and Northeast New Guinea and sold as walnut; a good hard, straight-grained wood; suitable for flooring.

Occurrence.—Throughout the region; common to abundant on alluvial flats and on lowland ridges.

FIGURE 68. *Dracontomelum sylvestre*

Dracontomelum sylvestre (Fig. 68)

Local Names. Raoe hoetan (Malayan).

Habit. A large tree, with pronounced buttresses.

Leaves. Pinnately compound, 12 to 18 in. long; leaflets 1½ by 5 in. to 2½ by 7 in., smooth above but with tufts of fine hairs at nerve axils below.

Flowers. Greenish-white, ¼ to ½ in. in diameter, borne in panicles which are frequently longer than the leaves.

Fruit. A drupe, 1 in. in diameter, depressed.

Wood. Light gray or greenish, with dark brown longitudinal stripes; grain crossed and occasionally wavy; texture fine; glossy; moderately hard, and tough; growth rings indistinct; pores diffuse, small to large, few in number; parenchyma inconspicuous, surrounding the pores; rays narrow, few in number; suitable for furniture and cabinet work, veneer, gunstocks; the wide buttresses are often made into table tops.

Occurrence. Andamans, Malay Peninsula, Borneo; allied species present in Indo-China, Hainan, Southern China, and Malay Archipelago.

FIGURE 69.—*Koordersiodendron pinnatum*

Koordersiodendron pinnatum (Fig. 69)

Local Names.—Philippines: Tirong, oris, uris, urisan (Cagayan, Ilocos Norte); taligaan (Ilocos Norte); salga, sarga (Ilocos Sur, Abra); molato (Abra); bankasi, bankalari (Ilocano); malabanais, marabanias, palapias (Pangasinan); orisen (Tarlac); dangila (Tagalog); ambugis, amugis, mugis (Bulacan, Bataan, Rizal, Laguna, Tayabas, Camarines, Albay, Marinduque, Palawan, Negros, Zamboanga); barok, pamalatangan (Sorsogon); karogkog (Bicolano); hamoges, hamogis, koro (Catanduanes); kalumanog, lakolako, sambalagan (Bisaya); sambulauan (Masbate, Samar, Leyte, Capiz, Cebu, Surigao); kia-kia (Cebu); maguyabud, sinambuauan (Surigao); magmakopa (Misamis); mariganda, samboan, sinambuauan (Agusan); kalantas-colorado (Cotabato); saba-uauan (Manobo); bugis, maguahod (Davao); gagil, magalibas, magulibas (Zamboanga, Davao, Sulu).

Habit.—A large tree to 60 in. in diameter and with a main stem of 35 to 55 ft.; straight, only small buttresses.

Leaves.—Pinnately compound, alternate, bunched at the ends of twigs; 13 to 16 pairs of leaflets; leaflets 1 to 2½ in. by 3½ to 8 in.; smooth, glossy, green above, yellowish-green below, veins usually bright red; main leaf stem is hairy. The tree is evergreen although the crown is considerably thinner during the dry season.

Flowers.—Small, in terminal drooping racemes.

Fruit.—A drupe.

Bark.—Dark brown, 4 to 7½ in. thick, strongly ridged; inner bark is pink to red with vertical bands of very light pink beneath the furrows; fibrous, exudes a gum which is used in local medicine.

197

Wood.—The sapwood is 1½ to 2½ thick, light pink, sharply demarcated from reddish to reddish-brown heartwood; rays narrow, moderately numerous, lighter in color than surrounding tissue, sinuous about the pores; pores nearly all isolated, evenly distributed, surrounded by parenchyma, moderately small, tyloses visible in all pores of the heartwood; parenchyma indistinct and surrounds each pore with a narrow ring; specific gravity air-dry 0.674; grain is crossed and often wavy, texture fine, without definite taste or odor, glossy, fairly heavy, subject to warping during seasoning, works easily and takes high finish; moderately durable when exposed or in contact with the ground; is suitable for flooring and has been used for general house construction, furniture and cabinet making.

Occurrence.—Celebes and widely distributed throughout Philippines on most islands and occurs in open forest and at low altitudes; is not abundant.

FIGURE 70.—*Mangifera minor*

Mangifera minor (Fig. 70)

Local Names.—New Guinea: Ewa (Buna), dua (Yalu, Lower Markham Valley), ihara (Suku), auroro (Vailala).

Habit.—Attains 3 ft. in diameter and clear length of 50 ft.; without buttresses.

Leaves.—Simple, alternate, petiole 1 to 2 in. long, twisted; blade 8 to 11 in. by 1 to 3 in., lanceolate, thin, smooth.

Flowers.—Borne in axillary panicles 7 to 8 in. long at ends of branchlets.

Fruit.—Stringy, nearly fleshless mango.

Bark.—Light brown, ½ in. thick, light brown, mango odor; inner bark pale yellow; sap is poisonous in contact with the skin.

Wood.—Sapwood not demarcated from heartwood; white with slight saffron tinge; rays 240 per in., brown, sinuous around pores, appears as brown specks on radial surface; pores conspicuous, 1,400 to 2,000 per sq. in., irregularly distributed, occasional diagonal chains, sometimes contain black deposit; parenchyma in fine concentric lines, wavy, connect the pores; specific gravity 0.722; cuts firm and clean; straight-grained; good for general construction.

Occurrence.—Throughout the region; common on alluvial flats and low ridges, extends up mountain slopes to 2,000 ft.

FIGURE 71.—*Pleiogynium solandri*

Pleiogynium solandri (Fig. 71)

Local Names.—Vasapa (Suku, New Guinea).

Habit.—A large tree to 36 in. in diameter with 75 ft. of main stem; buttresses to 4 ft. up the trunk.

Leaves.—Borne crowded at ends of branchlets, pinnately compound, alternate; stalk 7 to 9 in. long, leaflets 5 to 6 pairs with a terminal one, subopposite or opposite; leaflets with short petioles, blade 1 to 2 in. x 2 to 4 in., smooth margins, glabrous, elliptical.

Flowers.—Axillary.

Fruit.—¾ in. in diameter, with red, fleshy outer coating, containing a hard, crown-shaped nut; flowers and fruits in May and June.

Bark.—Gray, ½ in. thick, with rough ridges; inner bark streaked with white; exudes a small flow of sticky, whitish sap.

Wood.—Sapwood pale pink, 3 in. thick; heartwood dark brown; rays pinkish-yellow, wavy with large sweeping curves, appearing as specks on the radial surface; pores occur singly and are arranged in zones; parenchyma in very thin rings about 1 per in.; specific gravity, air-dry 0.914; slightly cross-grained. Probably suitable for cabinet work but the interlocked grain may make it difficult to work.

Occurrence.—This species has been found in Philippines and in southern New Guinea.

FIGURE 72.—*Semecarpus decipiens.*

Semecarpus decipiens (Fig. 72)

Habit.—Medium to large tree.

Leaves.—Very large, grayish below.

Bark.—Contains sap which turns black upon exposure and is very caustic. Care must be taken in handling this species; skin irritation is similar to that caused by poison ivy and treatment is the same.

Wood.—Fairly soft; has possibilities as a light construction wood.

Occurrence.—In the rain forest of lowlands and lower mountain slopes, throughout the region; this is one of several species in this genus.

FIGURE 73.—*Spondias pinnata*

Spondias dulcis (see Fig. 73 for another species)

Local Names.—Iopeia (Vailala), kara (Evara).

Habit.—Attains 30 in. in diameter and 100 ft. in height with 60 ft. of main stem; it bears spur roots but is not buttressed.

Leaves.—Compound, alternate, stalk 12 to 17 in. long; leaflets 5 to 8 pairs, opposite or nearly so; blade 2 to 5 in. by 3 to 6 in., obovate or lanceolate, with finely toothed margins, distinct veins, leathery. The stalk when crushed yields an odor resembling mango.

Flowers.—White, small, borne in erect terminal panicles.

Fruit.—Yellow and ovoid drupe, 2 in. in diameter. Encloses a corrugated, woody nut, with about five seeds.

Bark.—About ¾ in. thick, gray, bears longitudinal lines; inner bark white, streaked with yellow.

Wood.—Gray in color; sapwood not sharply demarcated from heartwood; rays brown, indistinct on cross-section, appear as minute brown squares on the radial surface; pores conspicuous, evenly distributed, parenchyma surrounding the pores; specific gravity, air-dry, 0.449; cuts soft but woolly.

Occurrence.—New Quinea.

Icacinaceae

(Icacina Family)

172. This family consists of about 45 genera and 150 species of trees, shrubs and woody vines which are widely distributed throughout the tropics. The giant climbers of this family in the region yield a large amount of good drinking water when cut. In this family also is the genus *Villaresia,* the leaves of which are a suitable substitute for those of *Ilex* in producing "mate" in Brazil, Paraguay and Argentina.

Gonocaryum calleryanum (Fig. 74)

Local Names.—Busigan, malapinggan, maligagak, maligapok, maragauid (Cagayan) · kuliuan (Isobela); uratan (Ilocos Norte); maragauan (Ilocos Norte, Pangasinan); rogrogso (La Union); malaikmonglalaki (Nueva Ecija); malasituin (Pampanga); anilao (Zambales); malapinggan (Bataan, Laguna); malasamat (Bataan, Batangas); lunas (Bataan, Rizal, Laguna); pinggan-pinggan (Tayabas); malatapai (Camarines).

Habit.—Attains 25 in. in diameter with 15 to 30 ft. of clear length; trunk is straight but has small buttresses.

Leaves.—Simple, alternate, 7 to 8 in. long by 4 in. wide, elliptical, leathery, with entire margins, light green above and lighter below.

Flowers.—Small white, borne in racemes attached at axils of the leaves.

Fruit.—A drupe, $\frac{1}{2}$ to $\frac{3}{4}$ in. in diameter, tough and woody.

Bark.—Dark gray.

Wood.—Sapwood is not sharply demarcated from the pinkish-tan heartwood; growth rings are indistinct; rays are broad, few in number, presenting a silvery appearance on the radial surface; parenchyma diffuse, distinct, extending between the rays or between vessels and rays, very numerous; specific gravity, air-dry, 0.614 to 0.758, average 0.734; straight grained, fine textured, without distinct taste or odor, fairly heavy, moderately hard and strong, seasons well, works and finishes well; durable for interior work but not durable when exposed or in contact with the ground. It is suitable for furniture and cabinet work, for making veneer and plywood, and for household utensils.

208

Occurrence.—Philippines; Batanes Islands and Luzon in virgin forests at low and medium altitudes up to 2,250 ft.; common in Bataan, where a good supply is obtainable.

FIGURE 74.—*Gonocaryum calleryanum*

Sapindaceae

(Soapberry Family)

Trees, shrubs, and herbs confined chiefly to hot countries, but some are found also in temperate regions of the northern hemisphere. The inner bark and the fruits of many species contain saponin; leaves compound, alternate or rarely opposite, with an odd leaflet; a number of the species produce useful wood.

FIGURE 75.—*Cubilia blancoi*

Cubilia blancoi (Fig. 75)

Local Names.—Kamilo, kiriron, kinidow, kinilow, araran (N. Celebes); amasi (Moluccas); boewa asa, B. poewasa, B. sanrangang (Makassar); boewa latji, B. sanrangang (Boegina). Philippines: malasanguing (Tagalog); cubili (Bulacan); lubilubili (Bataan).

Habit.—A large tree, attaining 90 to 120 ft. in height.

Leaves.—Alternate, pinnately compound, about 16 in. long, with 5 to 6 pairs of leaflets.

Folwers.—Very small, borne in open panicles about 6 in. long.

Fruit.—One to 2 in. long by about $3/4$ in. wide; seeds have chestnut-like taste and may be cooked and eaten.

Wood.—Light reddish-brown; pores small but numerous.

Occurrence.—Widely distributed throughout the Philippines at low and medium altitudes; extensively cultivated for its fruit in Moluccas and Celebes.

FIGURE 76.—*Euphoria didyma*

213

Euphoria didyma (Fig. 76)

Local Names.—Alupung, marutong, pamirigin, dinopa (Cagayan, Isabela); apalung (Cagayan, Isabela, Tayabas); bakalao, bukkalao (Cagayan, Isabela, Ilocos Norte, Ilocos Sur, Pangasinan, Zambales); alpai, aluak, alupag, alupag kalabau, alupai, alupao, alupi, aropag, arupag, ayupag, halupag, kalupai, lupak, ropag, rupar (Cagayan, Isabela, Ilocos Norte, Ilocos Sur, Zambales, Pangasinan, Nuevia Ecija, Tarlac, Pampanga, Bataan, Laguna, Tayabas, Mindoro, Panay, Sulu); suket (Ilocos Norte); balamban (Ilocos Sur); aning-vai moling (Pangasinan); paetan-nakir (Zambales); bait, taningi, tinaingi (Bataan, Tayabas); kandongisol, karabdab (Albay, Masbate); panuto (Masbate); kagasakas (Catanduanes); matobato (Catanduanes, Samar); balik (Mindoro); balit (Negros); maglolosong (Samar); esau, ulayan, usau (Leyte); kalisankad, kuluris, malabato (Palawan); buan-ubak, lupal (Cotabato); bolik, mamata (Zamboanga); bakuyong, lupak, lupanga (Sulu).

Habit.—A medium sized tree attaining 40 in. in diameter with a main stem of 30 to 35 ft.; trunk generally fluted and seldom straight; buttresses are heavy and low.

Leaves.—Pinnately compound with leaflets variable in size and shape, elongated, with entire margins.

Flowers.—Small, greenish or yellowish, borne in many flowered panicles.

Fruit.—A small ellipsoidal drupe containing 1 seed.

Bark.—Smooth, may be mottled.

Wood.—Sapwood 1 to 1½ in. thick, light red, not sharply demarcated from the tan heartwood; rays very narrow, indistinct, numerous; pores isolated, few, in groups of 2 to 3; some deposits of light to reddish-yellow substance; specific gravity, air-dry, 0.879 to 1.114, average 0.972; straight grained, fine textured, glossy, without distinct taste or odor; heavy, hard, strong; seasons well and easily; difficult to work but takes a high finish; durable when exposed and moderately resistant to marine borers; has been used for posts, sills, beams, rafters, flooring, wooden anchors, combs, parts of agricultural implements, salt water priming, keels of ships, and other purposes for which an unusually hard, heavy wood is required.

Occurrence.—Widely distributed but not abundant throughout the Philippines at low and medium altitudes.

FIGURE 77. *Euphoria longana*

Euphoria longana (Fig. 77)

Local Names. Kyet-mouk (Burma); mata kuching, lengkeng (Malayan).

Habit. Attains 30 to 50 ft. in height and 1 to 2 ft. in diameter with a clear length of 15 to 25 ft.; trunk not generally straight, somewhat fluted; thick, low buttresses at the base.

Leaves. Pinnately compound; leaflets 3 to 4 pairs, 3 to 4 in. long, lanceolate, with smooth margins, leathery, glossy on upper surface, with whitish bloom below, borne on short, thick petioles.

Flowers. Small, yellowish-white, on short peduncles, borne in terminal panicles.

Fruit. Globose, about the size of a cherry, with dry, hard outer coating, containing a single seed, and surrounded by a fleshy white edible pulp.

Wood. Sapwood 1 to 2 in. thick, light red, not sharply demarcated from the tan heartwood; growth rings distinct, demarcated by the dense late wood and a narrow band of terminal parenchyma; pores isolated or in groups of 2 to 3, evenly distributed, some with light yellow to reddish deposits; parenchyma terminal and surrounding pores; terminal parenchyma very narrow; rays very narrow, indistinct, very numerous; texture fine; with glossy appearance, without characteristic taste or odor; heavy, hard, strong; specific gravity, air-dry, 0.879 to 1.114 average 0.972; seasons well with very little defect, difficult to work; takes a high polish; durable when exposed and fairly resistant to marine borers; has been used for posts, beams, rafters, flooring, parts of agricultural implements, salt-water piling, keels of ships, and for other purposes for which a hard, heavy, and fairly durable wood is required.

Occurrence. In the forests at low and medium altitudes, but is not abundant; both wild and cultivated; Burma, Indo-China, Siam, Malay Peninsula, South China.

218

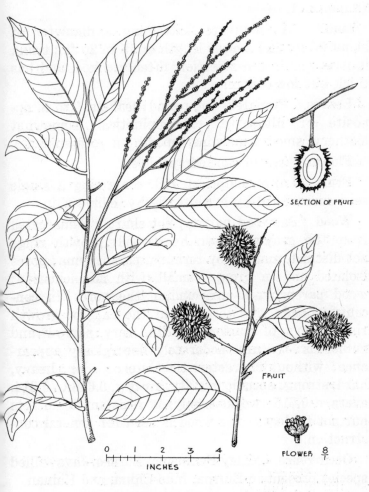

SECTION OF FRUIT

FRUIT

FLOWER $\frac{8}{1}$

0 1 2 3 4
INCHES

FIGURE 78. *Nephelium mutabile*

Nephelium mutabile (Fig. 78)

Local Names. Poelasan, pulasan, sangga lotong (Malayan); toekou biawak (W. Borneo); kapoelasan (Sunda Is.).

Habit. A small tree, attaining a diameter of about 25 in. and a clear length of 15 to 20 ft.; trunk is irregular in cross section, often crooked, and has thick but low buttresses.

Leaves. Pinnately compound; leaflets 4 to 8, opposite or alternate, oblong-elliptical, somewhat leathery, smooth margins, smooth on both surfaces.

Flowers. Small, borne in panicles.

Fruit. Large, elliptical, red, containing a single seed surrounded by a white, fleshy, edible pulp.

Wood. Sapwood narrow, not sharply demarcated from the grayish-brown heartwood; growth rings not distinct, marked by terminal parenchyma; pores isolated and in groups, small, with no inclusions; wood parenchyma surrounding the pores, in concentric bands, and terminal at the ends of growth rings; rays of uniform width, very narrow and numerous; texture moderately fine; glossy appearance; without characteristic taste or odor; heavy, hard, strong; specific gravity, air-dry, 0.616 to 0.814, average 0.715; works easily, is resistant to insects but not to decay; the wood is used for general construction.

Occurrence. Malay Peninsula, Borneo, Java; allied species present in Burma, Indo-China, and Hainan.

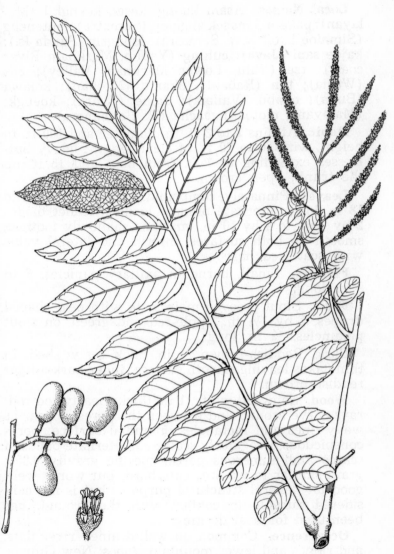

FIGURE 79. —*Pometia pinnata.*

221

Pometia pinnata (Fig. 79)

Local Names. Asam kuang, kasai, koengkil (Malayan); pakam, langsek anggang (Sumatra); lauteneng (Simaloe I., off N.W. Sumatra); leungsir (Sunda Is.); kajoe sapi (Java); cuhing (Yabim, Markham River coast); tze (Yalu, Lower Markham Valley); bas (Waria); tun (Rabaul); okamu (Motuan); koiawa (Buna); ohabu (Vailala); daine (Evara); koengki (Malayan); motoa, ngaache (N. Halmahera).

Habit. Attains 2 to 3 ft. in diameter and 100 ft. in height, with 30 to 70 ft. of clear length; heavy buttresses extending to 7 ft. from base and 15 ft. up the trunk; open crown.

Leaves. Pinnately, compound, alternate; petiole to 18 in. long; alternate pinnate leaflets; leaflet blades 2 by 4 in. to 4 by 10 in., margins shallowly toothed, smooth on both surfaces, midrib and lateral veins with scattered hairs.

Flowers. Small, borne in axillary panicles, 6 to 9 in. long.

Fruit. Stout grooved main stalk with pear-shaped drupes, 1 by 1½ in., apple-red and green, on stout peduncles, ¼ in. long.

Bark. Reddish-brown, ¼ in. thick, scaly; sheds in thin flakes leaving smooth surface; inner bark a light reddish-brown.

Wood. Sapwood white, 1 in. thick; heartwood red; rays curve around and between the pores, appear as wavy lines and rectangles on radial surface; pores conspicuous, irregularly scattered, alternate bands of scarce and numerous pores; specific gravity 0.850; grain similar to walnut; cuts hard, but works well; good for general structural purposes but is not considered durable in contact with the ground; has been used for boat decking.

Occurrence. Common on well-drained river flats, and ridges and lower mountain slopes; New Guinea, Bismarcks, Solomons, Borneo, Malay States, Sumatra, Java.

FIGURE 80. –*Tristira triptera*

223

Tristira triptera (Fig. 80)

Local Names.—Malaropag, cahoy-dalaya (Philippines).

Habit.—A small tree about 40 ft. in height.

Leaves.—Pinnately compound, about 8 in. long with 4 to 6 pairs of nearly oblong leaflets.

Flowers.—Small, white, and borne in open panicles.

Fruit.—A rough drupe, 1 to 2 in. long by 1 in. wide; seeds 1 in. long, surrounded by a white fleshy edible aril; seeds may be eaten after either boiling or roasting.

Bark.—Gray.

Wood.—Light gray; rays very fine and numerous; pores isolated and in groups, fairly small, parenchyma in bands moderately broad and wavy; grain slightly wavy; growth rings marked by terminal parenchyma and denser wood.

Occurrence.—A small tree widely distributed throughout the Philippines at low and medium altitudes; also occurs in Celebes.

Rhamnaceae

(Buckthorn Family)

Trees and shrubs, often armed with spines; plants occur throughout the tropical and temperate zones. Leaves simple and entire or toothed. Fruit is from one to four-celled and capsular or drupaceous. The representatives are widely known chiefly by their bitter bark and berry-like fruits. *Rhamnus infectoria* and related species afford important coloring matter, while other members yield tannin, saponins, fats, and resin.

Zizyphus talanai (Fig. 81)

Local Names.—Aggok, aggub, aggug, diran (Cagayan); aligamen, pangapatuten (Ilocos Norte); diran, malabolak (Ilocos Sur); kalinga (Abra); agob (Mountain Province); diaan, dir-an, duplok (Pangasinan); duldap (Pangasinan, Zambales); balakat (Zambales, Nueva Ecija, Bataan, Laguna, Camarines, Palawan, Butuan); bia-a, dia-a (Zambales); dir-an, lanutan (Nueva Ecija); dur-an (Tarlac); agup (Bulacan); biaa (Rizal); biaa, bigaan, ligaa (Laguna); talanai (Tagalog); bigaa, digaa, ligaa (Butacan, Rizal, Tayabas, Leyte, Samar, Negros); diaan (Batangas); ligaa (Bataan, Camarines, Ablay, Samar, Leyte, Davao); dugaa (Sorsogon); gasabang (Catanduanes); bariango, bonglas, dagas, dagia, maglangka (Palawan); bungaa, malabiga (Negros Occidental); dagaao (Surigao, Agusan); daguo (Davao).

Habit.—A large tree attaining 60 in. in diameter with 35 to 55 ft. of main stem; large buttresses.

Leaves.—Alternate, small.

Flowers. — Small, greenish, with heart-shaped petals.

Fruit.—A globose drupe, with 3 to 5 seeds.

Bark.—Thin, checkered, corky, usually with large pyramidal spines.

Wood.—Sapwood narrow, not sharply demarcated from the light red heartwood; rays very narrow, indistinct, numerous; pores isolated and in groups of 2 to 5, evenly distributed, quite small; specific gravity air-dry 0.533 to 0.366, average 0.513; grain is straight, occasionally wavy; texture fine to coarse, without distinct taste or odor; moderately hard and strong, seasons well, works easily and takes a high finish; moderately resistant to insects but not durable in contact with the ground. It is used for general construction and ordinary furniture, and is suitable for the making of veneer and plywood.

Occurrence.—Philippines; widely distributed from northern Luzon to Palawan and Mindanao; of common occurrence in the forests at low altitudes. The supply is small.

FIGURE 81.—*Zizyhpus talanai*

227

Elaeocarpaceae

(Elaeocarpus Family)

Medium-sized trees distributed throughout the tropics; leaves alternate, glossy or dark-green; bark thick, rough, affords a permanent dye varying from light-brown to jet black and used extensively by natives for dyeing garments; fruits edible.

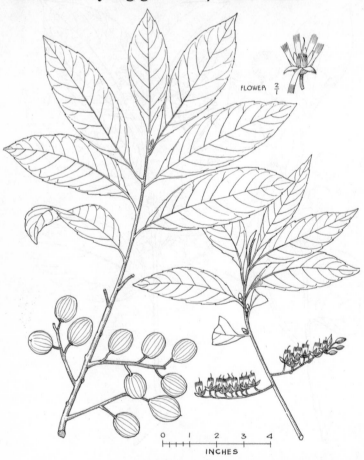

FLOWER $\frac{2}{1}$

FIGURE 82. *Elaeocarpus sphaericus*

228

Elaeocarpus sphaericus (E. ganitrus) (Fig. 82)

Local Names. Changkan (Malay Peninsula);
genitri (Java); klitri (Madura); ganitri (Bali).

Habit. Attains 40 to 50 ft. in height.

Leaves. Membranous, reddish when old, lanceolate but pointed at both ends, 1 by 3 in. to 2 by
5 in.; petioles ½ in. long.

Flowers. White, borne in racemes which are 3½
in. long with many flowers.

Fruit. A globose drupe, ¾ to 1 in. in diameter,
bright blue, with oily pulp and 5-celled stone or pit.

Wood. Sapwood white to grayish, heartwood yellowish to grayish-brown, lustrous, light to fairly
heavy, hard, fine-textured, straight- or wavy-
grained; growth rings distinct, marked by darker
zones or by terminal parenchyma; pores small, in
radial rows of 2 to 7, variable in size, evenly distributed; parenchyma absent, sparse, or terminal;
rays generally fine, numerous, yellowish-brown; durable for inside use but not when exposed or in contact with the ground; suitable for general light,
temporary construction, boxes, and furniture.

Occurrence. Malay Peninsula, Cochinchina, Formosa; many similar allied species (about 400) present in the region.

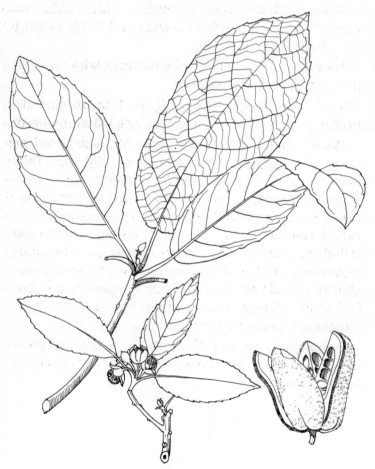

FIGURE 83.—*Sloanea brassii.*

Sloanea paradisiarum (see Fig. 83 for similar species)

Local Names.—New Guinea: oh-e (Buna), ofuni (Suku).

Habit.—Attains 2½ ft. in diameter and 100 ft. in height with clear length of 60 ft.; with buttresses.

Leaves.—Simple, alternate; petiole ½ to 2½ in.; blade 3 to 6 in. by 4 to 11 in., obovate, thin, smooth.

Fruit.—A hard woody capsule 1 to 2 in. by 2 to 4 in., bearing stiff bristles; splits open into three parts at maturity to release seeds.

Bark.—Gray, ¼ in. thick; inner bark yellow.

Wood.—White to grayish; sapwood not demarcated from heartwood; rays coarse and fine, coarse 72 per in., fine rays between coarse ones, sinuous around pores; pores conspicuous, 5,000 to 8,000 per sq. in., in zones, sometimes in groups of three; specific gravity 0.561; cuts soft and clean; good for light construction, inside work.

Occurrence.—Papua and Northeast New Guinea, perhaps also Bismarcks and Solomons; often one of commonest big trees on alluvial river flats, on ridges and lower mountain slopes; this is one of about 30 species in this genus.

Tiliaceae

(Linden Family)

Trees or shrubs; leaves alternate, simple, commonly deciduous; flowers usually perfect, sepals five, petals five or none; stamens usually numerous; fruit is one-celled, dry, drupaceous, does not open at maturity. Plants widely dispersed throughout the temperate and tropical parts of both hemispheres.

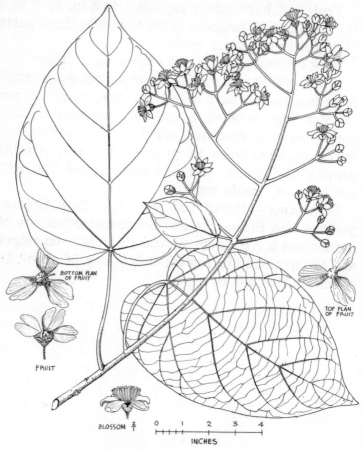

BOTTOM PLAN OF FRUIT

TOP PLAN OF FRUIT

FRUIT

BLOSSOM $\frac{2}{1}$

INCHES

0 1 2 3 4

FIGURE 84. *Berrya cordifolia*

232

Berrya cordifolia (Fig. 84)

Local Names. Hpekwoon (Burma); dok leung (Indo-China).

Habit. A medium-sized or large tree often from 75 to 100 ft. in height and 2 to 3 ft. in diameter; trunk usually fairly straight, cylindrical, and clear of branches for about one-half of the total height of the tree; crown dense and spreading.

Leaves. Simple, alternate, ovate, with smooth margins, smooth on both surfaces, 2 by 4 in. to 3 by 8 in.; petiole 1 to 2 in. long.

Flowers. Large, borne in terminal or axillary panicles.

Fruit. A dry capsule, 3- to 4-valved, each valve 2-winged; seeds 1 to 4 in each cell.

Bark. Smooth, dark brown; in old trees, often rough.

Wood. Sapwood light brown, heartwood dark reddish-brown; growth rings indistinct; pores nearly all in radially arranged groups of 2 to 3, numerous, nearly all filled with tyloses; parenchyma surrounding the pores, and in concentric bands, narrow, few to numerous; rays narrow, indistinct, few to numerous; texture fine, grain straight; dull in appearance, has a pungent odor when freshly cut, surface feels greasy; very heavy, strong, and tough; specific gravity, air-dry, 0.934; difficult to saw but works up well with tools; takes a high polish and is rated as a durable wood; used for high-grade construction, for tool handles, carving, and for other purposes requiring the properties of toughness and durability.

Occurrence. On elevated, well-drained areas; Burma, Siam, Malay Peninsula, Java, Borneo, and Indo-China.

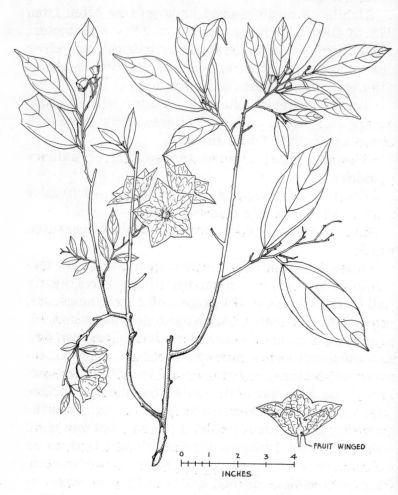

FRUIT WINGED

FIGURE 85. *Schoutenia mastersii*

Schoutenia mastersii (Fig. 85)

Local Names. Banitan merah, bayor bukit (Malay Peninsula).

Habit. Attains 8 to 10 in. in diameter and 50 to 80 ft. in height.

Leaves. Thin, leathery, glabrous and glossy green above, with fine brown hairs below, lanceolate or ovate, ½ by 1 in. to 1 by 3 in.; petiole 0.1 in. long.

Flowers. Borne singly in axils or in terminal panicles.

Fruit. Flat, 5-angled, inflated.

Wood. Suitable for general temporary construction.

Occurrence. Malay Peninsula and Borneo.

Malvaceae

(Mallow Family)

184. Trees, shrubs and herbs distributed throughout the tropical and warmer parts of the temperate zones. The great majority have leaves covered with hairs; bark affords tough fibers and mucilagenous soothing substances. The genus *Gossypium* yields cotton.

Hibiscus d'albertissii.

Local Names.—Variva (Suku, New Guinea).

Habit.—Attains 2 ft. in diameter and 60 ft. in height with 40 ft. of clear length; widely branched; without buttress but may have small spurs at base; a second story tree.

Leaves.—Simple, alternate, ovate, with smooth margins, 4 by 6 in., thin, smooth; petioles 1½ in. long.

Flowers.—Pink, 1½ by 3 in.

Bark.—Gray, fibrous, rough, ½ in. thick, inner bark white streaked with brown.

Wood.—Sapwood white or pale yellow, 2 in. thick; heartwood dark yellow or brown; rays 140 per in., brown, sinuous around pores, not distinct on radial surface; pores conspicuous, in zones, 1,300 to 1,600 per sq. in., evenly distributed; parenchyma in very fine lines between rays; specific gravity 0.625; cuts soft and clean; subject to a blue stain; durable in contact with ground; used for house posts.

Occurrence.—Throughout the region; on low river flats and ridges along coast and interior; in virgin forest, a medium-sized tree; in second growth rain forest, a small tree.

Bombacaceae
(Cotton-tree Family)

Trees widely distributed throughout the tropical parts of the world. Leaves simple or palmately compound and deciduous. Fruits are dry or fleshy and bear seeds often enveloped with silky fibers as in the silk-cotton tree *(Ceiba pentandra)*. Trees are often large and afford a relatively light-weight, though little-used wood.

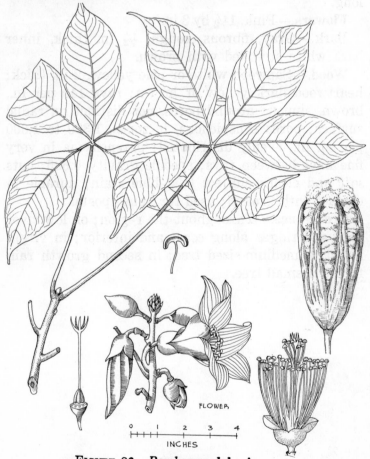

FLOWER

FIGURE 86. *Bombax malabaricum*

238

Bombax malabaricum (Gossampinus malabaricus)
(Fig. 86)

Local Names. Fromager; silk cotton tree; kapok kalingi (Malayan) ; dangdeur (Sunda Islands) ; randoe agoeng, randoe alas, randoe gembjang, randoe wana (Java) ; nanggher (Madura) ; kapok alas (Kangeang I., off N. E. Java) ; randeh, rangdoe (Bali) ; pardjong (Alor or Ombay I.)

Habit. A large tree, with a straight cylindrical trunk and buttresses at the base; branches in whorls, spreading horizontally.

Leaves. Large, palmately compound, with 5 to 7 leaflets.

Flowers. Large, scarlet, with fleshy petals.

Fruit. An elliptical, woody capsule, 5-celled and 4 to 6 in. long, with many seeds embedded in soft, silky hair.

Bark. Smooth, thick, grayish, may be armed with spines or prickles; on older trees, with longitudinal furrows.

Wood. Reddish-brown; grain straight or wavy, texture fine to coarse; growth rings generally indistinct; soft and weak; seasons quickly but is liable to staining if not properly handled; weight about 28 lbs. per cu. ft.; easy to work; not resistant to either insects or fungi; suitable for floats, boxes, crates, and temporary and emergency construction for which durability and strength are not necessary.

Occurrence. Generally at medium and low altitudes in virgin or second-growth forests, on flat sites, near river banks; Burma, Malay Peninsula, Indo-China, and Southern China.

239

Gossampinus heptaphylla

Local Names.—Silk cotton tree. Kapok kalingi (Malayan); makapok, koemana, kapes in taloen, makapes, mawekapes (N. Celebes); dandere (Makassar); tawar (Marind); kailoepa ma dorooe (N. Halmahera). Philippines: taroktok (Ilocos); bobor (Abra); boboo (Pangasinan); malabulak (Nueva Ecija, Bataan, Laguna, Tayabas); kapas-damo (Bataan); taglinan (Tagalog); babui-gubat (Rizal, Batangas, Mindoro, Palawan).

Habit.—Attains 36 in. in diameter with 45 ft. of clear length; trunk is straight and without buttresses.

Leaves.—Palmately compound, large, with 5 to 7 leaflets which are sharply pointed and with entire margins.

Flowers.—White or pink, petals with silky hairs.

Fruit.—Elliptical, 2 to 3 in. long, seeds many, brown and imbedded in the soft silky hairs.

Bark.—Thick, white to gray, may be armed with stout spines or prickles.

Wood.—Sapwood not sharply demarcated from the tan heartwood; rays moderately broad, straight, readily visible; pores isolated and in groups, diffuse, fairly small to large, few in number, mostly oblong; parenchyma diffuse, in fine tangential lines connecting the rays; specific gravity, air-dry, 0.270; grain is straight, texture coarse, without definite taste or odor, light in weight, soft and weak, seasons rapidly but liable to sap-stain if seasoned in the log; easy to work, subject to insect damage and perishable in contact with the ground; has been used for fish net floats, boxes, crates, and temporary construction.

Occurrence.—Philippines; Luzon, Mindoro, Camiguin de Misamis, and Mindanao; is found scattered in virgin and second growth forests at medium and low altitudes; supply is small, occasionally has been cultivated as an ornamental.

Sterculiaceae
(Sterculia or Cacao Family)

An extensive family; mostly large trees producing woods of widely varying character; leaves alternate, with smooth margins and palmately compound; flowers often very conspicuous and handsome; bark usually light-colored, smooth; easily recognized in the forest.

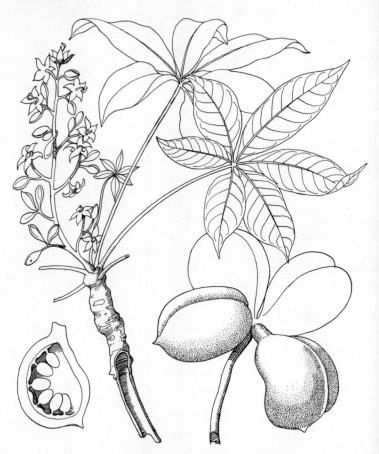

FIGURE 88. *Sterculia foetida*

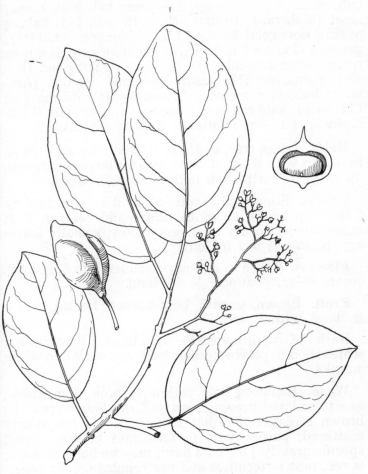

FIGURE 87. —*Heritiera littoralis.*

Heritiera littoralis (Fig. 87)

Local Names. Lookingglass tree, doengon, bekekan (Sumatra); bajoer laoet, atun laut, bayor laut, dungun, buah pelir kambing, doengoen, bebekan, atoeng laoet (Malayan); tjerlang laoet (Sunda Is.); balang pasisir, doengoen, lawang (Java); longon (Madura); genoera (Pantar I.); doengoe, lawanan kete, lawanan rintek, wolo i membe (N. Celebes); doengoeno (Boelo); roemoeng (Makassar, Boegina); loeloen (Ambon); leligen, roroemoe (Halmahera); kabi ma gosi (Ternate); kahi ma hoso (Tidore); dungon-kite (Philippines); pair-iru (Vailala); napera (Suku).

Habit. Large tree, to 3½ ft. in diameter and 100 ft. in height with 60 ft. of clear length; large buttresses, up to 12 ft.; butt often hollow in large trees.

Leaves. Simple, alternate; blade 2 by 4 in. to 4 by 6 in., elliptical or obovate; midrib and veins yellow; shiny above, brown or silvery below, smooth, leathery; petiole ¾ to 1 in. long.

Flowers. Borne in axillary panicles, 5 to 6 in. long, cream color; peduncle ⅛ in. long.

Fruit. Brown, smooth, boat-shaped, keeled. 2 to 3 in. long, with 1 seed.

Bark. Gray-brown, ½ in. thick; longitudinal scales shed in patches; inner bark red with fine white streaks.

Wood. Sapwood pale yellow to pink, 2 in. thick; heartwood red-brown; rays yellow, fine, appear as brown streaks on radial surface; pores irregularly scattered; parenchyma in fine lines between rays; specific gravity 1.01; cuts hard; may be hard to work; is resistant to termites and has reputation for resistance to marine borers; used for boatbuilding in Australia and for piling in the Philippines.

Occurrence. Throughout the region; common in mangrove association, also along river or mud flats up to limit of tidal influence.

Sterculia edelfeltia

Local Name.—Bakua (Suku).

Habit.—Attains 30 in. in diameter and with a 60 ft. main stem; buttresses often to 9 ft.

Leaves.—Simple, alternate; petiole 4 to 5 in. long; blade 3 to 5 in. x 4 to 9 in., lanceolate, smooth margins, slightly hairy on lower side but smooth surfaced on upper side.

Flowers.—Bell-shaped, borne in drooping panicles.

Fruit.—2½ to 3 in., contains 5 to 7 seeds.

Bark.—Smooth, gray; inner bark light brown.

Wood.—Pale yellow in color, sapwood not sharply demarcated from heartwood; rays conspicuous, both coarse and numerous and fine, generally straight, appear as gray, shiny bands on radial surface; pores large and conspicuous; specific gravity, air-dry, 0.368; straight grained, cuts very soft and woolly.

Occurrence.—New Guinea; collected near Veimauri, Vanapa and Aroa, Hydrographer's Range up to 2,000 ft., also on the Main Range.

Sterculia foetida (Fig. 88)

Local Names. Stinkmalve, haloempang (N. Sumatra, Battak country); kelumpang, keloempang, kepoeh (Malayan); kepoh, koleangka (Sunda Is.); djangkang, kepoh, poh (Java); djhangkang, kalompang (Madura); ghalompang (Kangean I., off N.E. Java); kekepahan (Bali); kajoembang, kapaka (Sumba); kepoh (Flores I.); woekak (Solor I.); woeka (Pantar I.). Philippines: hantak (Batanes); ani, bangad, bangog (Cagayan); bangar (Ilocos Sur, Abra, Isabela, Pangasinan); bubur (Ilocos Sur); alayag (Nueva Ecija, Pampanga, Bataan, Rizal, Manila, Laguna, Tabayas, Mindoro, Palawan, Iloilo, Cotabato); balinad (Camarines Norte); u-os (Camarines Sur); bobo, bubog (Iloilo, Negros); doldol (Palawan); kurumpang (Davao); kamuyao (Zamboanga); kumpang (Sula).

Habit. A large tree, to 50 in. in diameter, with 25 to 35 ft. of main stem; trunk is straight and regular.

Leaves. Crowded at ends of the branchelets; palmately compound, with 5 to 11 leaflets; blades of leaflets lanceolate or nearly oblong, pointed, thick, with entire margins.

Flowers. Borne in small panicles, dull red; bloom with unfolding of leaves and have very unpleasant odor.

Fruit. Large, woody, red, single-celled, 3 in. in diameter, with smooth surface; splits open along one side and contains black elliptical seeds, ¾ in. in length.

Bark. Ashy-gray, thick.

Wood. Sapwood tan, not sharply demarcated from the pink heartwood; rays moderately broad, few in number, lighter than surrounding elements; pores isolated and in groups, diffuse, small to large, oblong, few in number, tyloses present in all pores of heartwood; specific gravity, air-dry, 0.494 to 0.599; straight-grained, coarse-textured; without distinctive taste, but heartwood has a pungent odor; comparatively light, soft and weak; works and finishes well; durable in interior work and not durable when exposed or in contact with the ground; suitable for general building construction.

Occurrence. Throughout the region; usually along seashores and forest edges; has been very little utilized in the past.

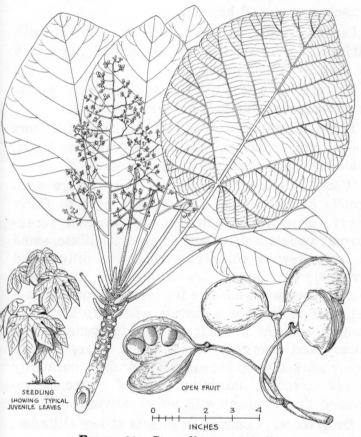

SEEDLING
SHOWING TYPICAL
JUVENILE LEAVES

OPEN FRUIT

0 1 2 3 4
INCHES

FIGURE 89. *Sterculia macrophylla*

Sterculia macrophylla (Fig. 89)

Local Names. Milian, kelumpang (Malay Peninsula); hantap, hantap heulang (Sunda I.); dok, kalong (Java); klowang (Madura).

Habit. Attains 60 to 120 ft. in height; young branches stout and hairy.

Leaves. Ovate, leathery, with fine hairs on both surfaces, 6 by 8 in. to 12 by 16 in.; petioles 3 to 6 in. long, with soft hairs.

Flowers. Borne in long, axillary, and many-branched panicles, which are 6 to 8 in. long.

Fruit. Leathery or woody, $2\frac{1}{4}$ in. long, with short stalks, pink to bright red, covered with fine hairs, contain oblong black seeds, $\frac{3}{4}$ in. long.

Wood. Light pink, grain straight, texture moderately coarse, weight ranges from light to fairly heavy; growth rings marked by terminal parenchyma; vessels isolated and in groups, diffuse, small to large, few in number; parenchyma diffuse and terminal; rays broad, few in number; works well and finishes well; durable for interior work but not resistant to fungi and insects when exposed or in contact with the ground; suitable for general temporary and emergency construction where a light, easily worked wood is required and where durability is not essential; durability may, of course, be increased by treatment with preservatives.

Occurrence. Common in forests at low altitudes; Malay Peninsula, Java, Borneo, Sumatra; numerous allied species present in the region.

248

FIGURE 90. *Tarrietia javanica*

Tarrietia javanica (Fig. 90)

Local Names.—Lumbayau (Misamis, Zamboanga, Basilan); lumbayau-bato, tutubungan (Zamboanga); dungon, lumbayau-batu (Basilan); buhanan (Tawi-tawi).

Habit.—A large tree to 65 in. in diameter, with 60 to 75 ft. of main stem; trunk generally straight with large buttresses.

Leaves.—Alternate, palmately compound, with 3 to 5 leaflets; leaflets smooth, from 1½ to 3 in. x 3 to 8 in.

Flowers.—Small, reddish, borne in terminal panicles.

Fruit.—A winged, single-seeded fruit similar to that of the maple.

Bark.—2½ to 3 in. thick; in young trees gray and mottled, in older trees light gray with brown patches where scales have been shed; scales regular, square or oblong; inner bark reddish-brown.

Wood.—Sapwood light, 1 to 2½ in. thick, heartwood reddish; growth rings indistinct, marked by rings of early and late wood; rays moderately broad, few in number, straight, appear moderately broad and produce a "silver" grain on the radial surface; pores in groups, evenly distributed, moderately small to large, few in number; parenchyma surrounded pores, are diffuse or scattered; specific gravity, air-dry, 0.655; straight grained, coarse textured, comparatively heavy and hard, without definite odor or taste; tough, seasons well, is easy to work and finish, glues and stains well, is durable for interior work and moderately durable when exposed or in contact with the ground. Has been used for furniture and cabinet making, interior finish, ship and boat planking, and the manufacture of plywood; has been sold commercially in foreign markets under the name "Philippine mahogany."

Occurrence.—Confined to the islands of Mindanao (Misamis, Lanao, Zamboanga and Cotabato) and Basilan in the Philippines, where it is common in virgin forests at low and medium altitude in association with the lauans and other members of *Dipterocarpaceae;* supply is fairly large. Probably other species of this genus are present in New Guinea.

Dilleniaceae
(Dillenia Family)

Trees and sometimes climbing shrubs with long thickish alternate leaves. Several of the species are handsome tall trees widely used for ornamental planting; leaves large averaging from one to two feet long, in young tree sometimes as much as 4 to 5 feet long.

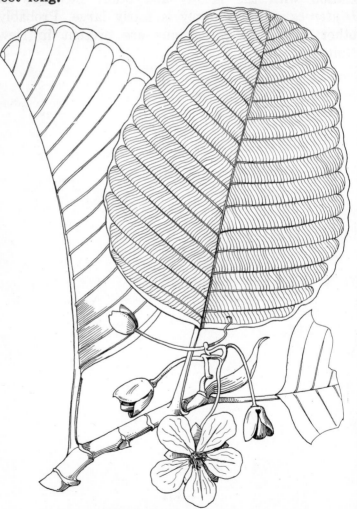

FIGURE 91. —*Wormia macrophylla.*

Wormia macrophylla (Fig. 91)

Habit.—A large tree, may have buttresses.

Leaves.—With winged petioles.

Bark.—Reddish - brown or bright orange - red, papery.

Wood.—Hard, has been utilized to some extent in Papua; probably good general purpose wood.

Occurrence.—Very abundant, on plains subject to flooding during rainy season; along Ramu River (New Guinea) and on New Ireland; several other tree species of this genus are common on ridges and mountain slopes throughout the region.

Theaceae

(Tea Family)

Tree and shrubs indigenous to the tropics; leaves simple, alternate, and usually evergreen; fruit usually a woody capsule with astringent and sedative properties.

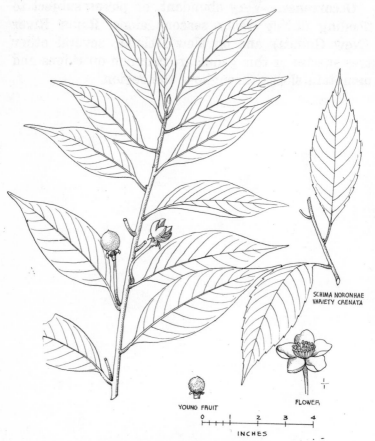

SCHIMA NORONHAE
VARIETY CRENATA

YOUNG FRUIT

FLOWER

INCHES

FIGURE 98. *Schima noronhae*

Local Names.—Mail (Likdin).

Habit.—Attains 2½ ft. in diameter and 100 ft. in height with 50 ft. clear length; without buttresses.

Leaves.—Simple, alternate; petiole ¼ in. long; blade 3 to 5 in. by 1 to 2 in., tapers equally to both ends; shallow indented margins, smooth, leathery.

Flowers.—White or cream-rose color; large single, at ends of branchlets.

Fruit.—Opens by five valves; seeds winged.

Bark.—Gray, large scales; inner bark streaked with brown and white; used by natives to poison fish.

Wood.—Sapwood white, not clearly demarcated from the yellow-rose heartwood; rays 250 per in., fine and coarse; coarse rays straight, fine ones sinuous around pores, appear as brown rectangles on radial surface; parenchyma in lines, connect coarse rays; grain crossed; specific gravity 0.769; should be suitable for uses where a dense tough wood is needed but may be difficult to saw and work up.

Occurrence.—At low elevations, Likden, New Ireland. This is one of several species of the genus from coastal lowlands up to middle elevation in the mountains in New Guinea and Solomons.

FIGURE 92. —*Gordonia papuana.*

Gordonia papuana (Fig. 92)

Local Names.—Mail (New Ireland).

Habit.—A large tree; trunk spurred but without large buttresses.

Bark.—Scaly.

Wood.—Fairly hard; should be generally useful but may be difficult to saw.

Occurrence.—New Guinea, Solomons; on ridges at low elevations near the sea; other species of genus occur in Bismarcks and Solomons.

Schima noronhae (Fig. 93)

Local Names. Kelat gelugor, medang bekawi (Malay States); simar toloe, madang boengkar, madang miang (Sumatra); hoeroe batoe, hoeroe manoek, poespa (Sunda Is.); poespa (Java).

Habit. Attains 40 to 50 ft. in height.

Leaves. Elliptical or lanceolate, leathery, 2 in. by 4½ in.; petioles ¾ to 1¼ in. long, flattened.

Flowers. Axillary or crowded at ends of branches, 1 to 1½ in. in diameter, white.

Fruit. Silky hairs when young, smooth when mature, ¼ in. to 5 in. in diameter.

Wood. Sapwood white, not sharply demarcated from the light reddish-brown heartwood; lustrous, works well, without distinctive taste or odor; fairly heavy, specific gravity about 0.72; grain irregular, texture medium; shrinks considerably during seasoning; considered durable for inside work; suitable for general construction of the semipermanent type.

Occurrence. Common in mountain forests at about 2,000 ft.; Malay Peninsula, Java, Borneo; similar allied species in Indo-China, Southern China, and Hainan.

Guttiferae
(Gamboge or Mangosteen Family)

Trees and shrubs growing in the tropical parts of eastern hemisphere; many species occur in India and Pacific islands. Plants generally acrid and yield yellowish gum-resins secreted by latex tubes (ducts) of the inner bark, sapwood, leaves, flowers, and fruit; leaves shiny, thick, and leathery; fruit hard or fleshy, those of *Garcinia* are edible; wood is valuable.

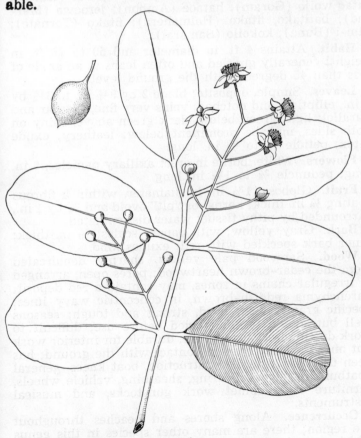

FIGURE 94. *Calophyllum inophyllum*

Calophyllum inophyllum (Fig. 94)

Local Names. Alexandrian laurel, benaga, bengga, bintangoer, bintangor bunga, penaga laut, pudek, penaga, metangoer (Malay Peninsula); ejobeh (Engano I., off S.W. Sumatra); poenaga, penago (Sumatra); naga, kanaga, panaga (Borneo); njamploeng (Sundra Is., Java, Madura); njalpong (Kangeang I., off N.E. Java); poenaga, tjamplong, mandara (Bali); mantaoe (Sumbawa); tapo (Pantar I.); dingkaran (N.W. Celebes); dingkaheng (Sangir); doenggala (Gorontalo); ilambe (Boelo); dongkalangi (Baree); poenaga (Makassar); ngoefar (Kai I.); bitao woijo (Goram); hataoe (Ambon); jeroewa (Marind); batitako, fitako (Halmahera); fitako (Ternate); otai-i (Buna); kokoilo (Samarai).

Habit. Attains 4 ft. in diameter and 50 to 75 ft. in height; generally gnarled and often leans at an angle of less than 45 degrees with the ground level.

Leaves. Simple, opposite; blade 2 by 3½ in. to 3½ by 6 in., elliptical and notched; veins very fine, regular and parallel; light green below, dark green above, shiny on both sides, midribs prominent below; leathery; exude latex; petiole ½ to ¾ in. long.

Flowers. White, borne in erect axillary panicles, 6 in. long; peduncle ¾ to 1¼ in. long.

Fruit. Globose, 1¾ in. in diameter, within a fibrous coating ⅛ in. thick; kernal or "pit" ovoid and ¾ by 1 in., surrounded by pithy tissue; water disseminated.

Bark. Gray, yellow; with papery scales; ½ in. thick; inner bark speckled with red; exudes kino.

Wood. Sapwood pale yellow, sharply demarcated from the cedar-brown heartwood; pores open, arranged in irregular chains in zones, may contain a red deposit; parenchyma reddish-brown, in concentric wavy lines; specific gravity 0.64; hard, strong and tough; seasons well but should be well dried before use; difficult to work due to interlocked grain; durable for interior work but only moderately so in contact with the ground; has been used for general construction, boat knees, general boatbuilding, doors, flooring, sheathing, vehicle wheels, furniture and cabinet work gunstocks, and musical instruments.

Occurrence. Along shores and beaches throughout the region; there are many other species in this genus which occur in the inland forests.

FRUIT

FIGURE 95. *Calophyllum wallichianum*

261

Calophyllum wallichianum (Fig. 95)

Local Names. Bintangor merah, bintangor akar, bintangor batu, bintangor bunga, bintangor labu, penaga batu, penaga ayer (Malay Peninsula); betoer (Banka I., off S.E. Sumatra); teroendjam (Billiton I., off S.E. Sumatra).

Habit. A tall tree; branchlets yellowish and 4-angled.

Leaves. Narrow, elliptical, 1½ by 5 in.; petioles ¾ in. long.

Flowers. About ½ in. broad.

Fruit. Globose, 1 in. in diameter.

Wood. Wood is light to dark red; grain straight, wavy, or crossed; texture fine, moderately hard; growth rings marked by rather indistinct terminal parenchyma; pores isolated, arranged in radial chains, small to large, few to fairly numerous, contain gummy deposits; rays narrow and numerous; suitable for general construction, ship and boat building, beams, flooring, gunstocks, etc.

Occurrence. Fairly common; Malay Peninsula.

FIGURE 96.—*Garcinia warburgiana.*

Garcinia hollrungii (see Fig. 96 for similar species)

Local Names.—Moka (Suku); pinuhunuhunu, naboita, sipego, matumatu, nakamolo (Bougainville).

Habit.—Attains 2 ft. in diameter and develops 60 ft. clear length; branching habit similar to conifers, continuous main stem.

Leaves.—Simple, opposite; petiole 3/4 to 1 in. long; blade obovate to elliptical, 7 by 4 in., smooth, leathery, stiff; stout twigs.

Fruit.—A pome, 2 by 2 in., green, yellow or red when ripe, has an acid flavor.

Bark.—Brown to greenish-black, 1/4 in. thick, exudes sticky yellow latex.

Wood.—White to yellow; sapwood not demarcated from heartwood; rays 130-135 per in., yellow, fine but conspicuous, sinuous around pores, appear as silver bands on radial surface; pores 2,000 to 3,000 per sq. in. fairly evenly distributed; parenchyma, in straight lines between rays; specific gravity 0.641; cuts clean; a good hard general purpose wood.

Occurrence.—New Guinea; this is one of many species in this genus occurring in the forests from sea level to high in the mountains, throughout the region.

Dipterocarpaceae

(Lauan or Dipterocarp Family)

Species mostly very large trees confined to the tropical parts of the eastern hemisphere; they range eastward from India through the Indian Archipelago and the Dutch East Indies to the Philippines and New Guinea; trunks tall and straight and of tremendous commercial importance; bark with resinous balsamic juices used as pitch, varnish, and medicine; leaves leathery; fruit with two wings in some genera, 3 to 5 in others, which suggest the name of the family. There are several hundred species in this family, nearly all of which are trees of the primary forests, and are good timber trees. They are especially prominent in Burma, Siam, Indo-China, Malay Peninsula, Sumatra, and Borneo. There are a few in Southern China and Hainan but they do not extend to Formosa. This is the most important timber tree family in the Far East.

FIGURE 97. *Anisoptera curtisii*

Anisoptera curtisii (Fig. 97)

Local Names. Mersawa, mentasawa, nenkong (Malay Peninsula).

Habit. A large tree attaining 30 to 40 in. in diameter, may attain as much as 80 in. in diameter with a clear length of 60 to 90 ft.; small buttresses.

Leaves. Simple, tapering toward both ends, upper surface smooth and shiny, lower surface with fine hairs along the veins, 1 by 3½ in.; petiole 1 in. long.

Flowers. Borne in panicles, 5 to 7 in. long, flowers greenish-white, ½ in. long.

Fruit. Small, globose or ovoid, 2-winged.

Wood. Sapwood lighter than the buff or reddish-yellow heartwood; growth rings indistinct; pores generally isolated, diffuse, with tyloses; parenchyma diffuse and around pores; resin ducts diffuse, small, few in number; rays narrow to quite broad, few in number, lighter than the surrounding tissue; grain crossed, texture fine, dull in appearance; with resinous odor when fresh but without characteristic taste or odor when dry; heavy, hard; specific gravity, air-dry, 0.646 to 0.817, average 0.745; seasons well, but is difficult to saw, takes a high finish, rated as medium in durability; used for interior finish, ship planking, furniture, plywood, and general construction work.

Occurrence. Malay Peninsula, Siam, Borneo; similar allied species present in Indo-China, Burma, and Malay Archipelago.

Anisoptera polyandra

Local Names.—Garawa (Buna), karawa or warawa (Binandele), Karalaka (Vailala).

Habit.—A large tree to 4 ft. in diameter, 130 ft. in height and with a clear length of 100 ft.; without buttresses.

Leaves.—Simple, alternate; blade oblanceolate, glabrous, yellow to rust colored below, light green above.

Fruit.—A nut, 7/8 in. long, enclosed in a coating, 2 lobes of which are extended to form spatulate wings.

Bark.—Gray with tinge of reddish-brown, with longitudinal lines up the trunk but flat ridges at base; inner bark streaked with yellow.

Wood.—Sapwood pale yellow, not clearly demarcated from heartwood; heartwood light buff, often with rose-colored longitudinal streaks; rays 110 per in., yellow, appear as wavy lines on radial surface; pores about 5,000 per sq. in., evenly distributed between the rays; parenchyma indistinct, in fine concentric rings, about 3 per in.; grain is straight; resinous; specific gravity about 0.690.

Occurrence.—Forms nearly pure stands, often with *Afzelia bijuga*, in foothills of Hydrographer's Range (New Guinea) up to about 1,000 feet. Good stands reported along the Kumusi River, behind Buna Bay and lower slopes of Hydrographer's Range.

FIGURE 98.—*Anisoptera thurifera*

269

Anisoptera thurifera (Fig. 98)

Local Names.—Duyong, guong (Ilocos Norte, Ilocos Sur, Nueva Ecija); apnit, duong (Abra); afu (Isabela); baliuasuas (Nueva Vizcaya); palosapis (Pangasinan, Nueva Ecija, Zambales, Bataan); babuisuis, barakbak, bariuisuis (Pangasinan); apis-apis, kumpol, lanum-put (Nueva Ecija); palihapi, mayapis (Zambales); dadang, mayapis (Bulacan, (Bataan, Rizal, Mindoro); basapis, pisapis (Bataan); dagang, dagang na puti lauaan, mala-atis (Rizal); dagang, dagum (Laguna, Albay); manapo (Polillo); dagang, tabila (Camarines); malanha (Albay); dagang (Catanduanes); makaasim, betis, letis (Masbate); bagobahong, lavan ng busay (Samar); letis (Ticao, Panay); pakpakan (Negros Occidental).

Habit.—A large tree, 40 to 50 in. in diameter with 60 to 90 ft. of main stem, without buttresses.

Leaves.—1½ to 3½ in. x 4½ to 8 in., yellowish, without hairs.

Flowers.—White or pink, with anise-like odor, borne in small clusters.

Fruit.—Dry and two-winged.

Bark.—7½ to 12½ in. thick; in young trees, smooth and yellowish, in older trees, broken into choppy pieces, dull brown; inner bark yellowish-brown, granular.

Wood.—Sapwood 2½ to 3½ in. thick, not sharply demarcated from the heartwood; heartwood is yellow with occasional pink streaks; rays fairly narrow, few in number; pores isolated or in groups, diffuse, small to large, oval, few in number; tyloses present; parenchyma surrounding the pores in narrow rings, also diffuse, in single, scattered strands; resin canals diffuse, few in number, very small,

270

filled with whitish resin when dry; specific gravity air-dry 0.613 to 0.821, average 0.710; grain crossed, texture fine to coarse, without characteristic taste, resinous odor when fresh, comparatively heavy and hard; is inclined to shrink excessively and requires careful seasoning; difficult to saw, very durable for interior work and moderately so when exposed or in contact with the ground; used for interior finish, ship planking, frames of vehicles, furniture making, veneer, plywood and general construction.

Occurrence.—Philippines; widely distributed on Luzon, Mindanao, Ticao, Masbate, Sibuyan, Panay, and Negros, in virgin forests at low altitudes; also along streams in second growth forests; available in large quantities; other species in this genus present in New Guinea.

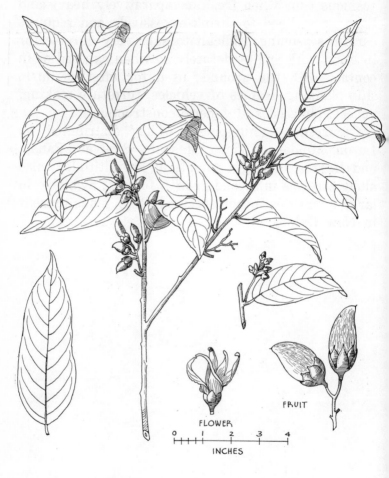

FLOWER

FRUIT

0 1 2 3 4
INCHES

FIGURE 99. *Balanocarpus heimii*

Balanocarpus heimii (Fig. 99)

Local Names. Tjengal, chengal, chengai, chengai batu, penak, penak bunga, penak sabut, penak lilin, penak tambaga (Malay States).

Habit. A large tree, may attain 60 in. in diameter and 200 ft. in height with 125 ft. of clear length; trunk is somewhat irregular but with very little taper and medium-sized buttresses at the base; crown is rather open and usually less than ½ the total height of the tree.

Leaves. Simple, alternate, leathery, sharply pointed, round at the base, upper surface glabrous and pale green, lower surface glabrous, may be pubescent along the veins, 1 by 2½ in. to 2 by 7 in.; petiole 0.3 to 0.4 in. long.

Flowers. Pale yellow, borne in small axillary clusters 4 to 6 in. long; individual flowers usually under ½ in. long.

Fruit. Ovoid, green, smooth, 2 to 2½ in. long; the base is covered by a persistent cup, a remnant of the flower.

Bark. Dark brown with purplish tint, with narrow longitudinal fissures; outer bark hard and brittle with small exudations of resin at the edges of fissures or at points of injury; inner bark yellow, fibrous, resinous, and with distinct ripple marks which turn dark brown after exposure.

Wood. Sapwood is narrow, sometimes only ¾ in. thick, considered worthless, sharply demarcated from the yellow to dark brown heartwood; hard, heavy, strong, straight-grained, relatively easy to work but is very difficult to season properly; rays distinct, fine and regular; pores small and diffuse; resin canals present; weight 37 to 51 lbs. per cu. ft.; specific gravity 0.59 to 0.81; larger logs are liable to have heartrot at the center; wood may have many pinholes caused by small wood borers but they do not lower the strength or affect durability a great deal and are not considered a defect on the commercial market; wood is subject to dry rot and when infected, the wooden member may fail in a short time; it is not immune to termite attack but is fairly resistant; the wood has been used for a wide variety of general construction work and for furniture, railroad ties, bridge timbers, and posts.

Occurrence. It is not known to occur outside the Malay Peninsula. It grows under a wide range of conditions and is found from sea level to 1,800-ft. elevation, always in dense forests; it occurs on low, flat, swampy areas and on gentle slopes or steep ridges but apparently makes its best development on the better-drained sites; it may be considered well represented when there occurs as many as 1 tree of commercial size to 2 acres of forest; generally distributed in the Malay Peninsula.

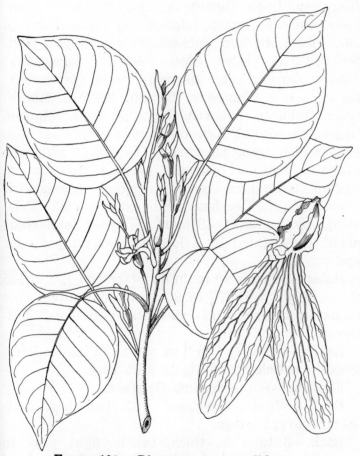

FIGURE 100. —*Dipterocarpus grandiflorus*

Dipterocarpus grandiflorus (Fig. 100)

Local Names.—Philippines: Keroewing, gombang (Malayan, Moluccas); duko, kamuyao, palalian, pamalalian, pamalalien (Cagayan); pamariusen (Cagayan, Ilocos Norte); apitong (Cagayan, Zambales, Bulacan, Bataan, Laguna, Tayabas, Camerines Sur, Albay, Mindoro, Palawan, Samar, Negros Occidental); pamantulen (Ilocos Norte, Pangasinan); duko, malapaku, kuku (Isabela); acete (Zambales); panae, panau (Zambales, Bataan, Bulacan, Rizal); balau (Bulacan, Palawan, Capiz, Misamis, Sibuyan, Negros Occidental, Agusan, Zamboanga); pagsahingin, pagsahingan, palsaingin (Laguna); malapaho (Tayabas); panau, malapalis, anahauon, panalsalan, aganan (Camarines Sur); hagakhak (Camarines, Samar, Negros Occidental, Sibuyan); alakak (Palawan), himpagkatan (Samar). "Bagac" is a trade name, copyrighted by a local lumber company for apitong.

Habit.—Attains 90 in. in diameter and 120 to 135 ft. in height with 75 to 90 ft. of main stem; the trunk is straight and cylindrical with small buttresses.

Leaves.—Simple, 4 to 8 in. x 9 to 15 in., leathery, smooth; petioles from 2½ to 3 in. long.

Flowers.—White or pink, fragrant.

Fruit.—Woody, one-celled, with two large, outwardly-curved wings.

Bark.—3 to 4 in. thick, brittle, light gray to brownish-gray, sheds large scroll-shaped plates and bears many corky pustules; inner bark reddish.

Wood.—Sapwood 2½ to 3 in. thick, not sharply demarcated from the reddish-brown heartwood; rays very narrow, few in number; pores isolated, small to

276

large, oblong, few in number; resin ducts surrounded by bands of parenchyma, fairly small, few in number; specific gravity, air-dry, 0.756 to 0.864, average 0.809; grain is crossed, texture from fine to coarse, without distinctive taste but has a slightly resinous odor; it warps and shrinks unless carefully seasoned, fairly hard to work but takes a high finish; durable for interior work, perishable in contact with the ground; absorbs preservatives readily, is suitable for posts, beams, rafters, flooring, bridge and dock construction, piling (preservative treated), car construction, furniture, telephone poles (preservative treated), and other purposes for which a hard, heavy wood is required.

Occurrence.—Philippines; Northern Luzon to Mindanao and Palawan; of common occurrence in virgin forests and at low and medium altitudes; available in fairly large quantities.

Local Names. Keruing chayer, keruing beku, keruing laut (Malay Peninsula) ; lagan (N.W. Sumatra, Achin country, and S. Sumatra) ; keroewing boenga (Simaloe I.) ; palahlar (Sunda Is.) ; klalar, plalar (Java) ; tampoerau (S.E. Borneo).

Habit. Attains about 60 in. in diameter and 100 to 125 ft. in height with a clear length of 60 to 75 ft.; trunk is generally straight and regular.

Leaves. Simple, ovate, 4 by 7 in. to 6 by 10 in., upper surface glabrous, lower surface glabrous or with veins covered with fine hairs, petioles ½ to 2½ in. long.

Flowers. Borne 2 to 8 together, 3 in. long.

Fruit. A nut, ovate, 1 in. in diameter, covered with fine tan hairs, 2 wings.

Wood. Sapwood lighter than the light to dark red heartwood; growth rings indistinct; pores isolated, few, in groups, diffuse, some tyloses present; parenchyma diffuse, and surrounding the pores, very narrow; resin ducts isolated, diffuse, small; rays of 2 distinct widths, quite narrow, few in number; grain is crossed or wavy; texture fairly coarse; dull in appearance, without characteristic taste or odor; heavy, hard, and strong; specific gravity, air-dry, 0.675 to 0.920, average 0.777; used for beams, rafters, flooring, furniture, bridge and dock construction, including piling and telephone poles when treated with preservatives.

Occurrence. Malay Peninsula, Java, Borneo; allied species present in Burma and Indo-China.

FIGURE 101 *Dipterocarpus oblongifolius*

279

Dipterocarpus oblongifolius (Fig. 101)

Local Names. Neram, nerrum, denderam, meneram, mengeram, keruing beku (Malay Peninsula).

Habit. Attains 40 to 80 ft. in height.

Leaves. Leathery, smooth, slenderly elliptical, 2 by 6 in. to 2½ by 8 in.; petiole 1 in. long.

Flowers. Borne in axillary panicles which are 6 in. long; flowers cream with rose tint, ½ by 2 in.

Fruit. Pink and glabrous when ripe, 5-ridged, 1¼ in. long, 2-winged.

Wood. Sapwood light in color, not sharply demarcated from the reddish-brown heartwood; grain crossed, texture moderately fine; dull in appearance; without distinctive taste but may have a resinous odor; hard, heavy and strong; growth rings indistinct; pores generally isolated, diffuse; parenchyma surrounding the pores and diffuse; resin ducts arranged in short arcs surrounded by parenchyma and may contain white resin; rays narrow to fairly broad, few in number; has been used for general construction requiring a strong, durable wood, especially for beams, rafters, flooring, bridges and wharfs, and for salt water piles, telephone and telegraph poles when treated with preservatives.

Occurrence. Often overhanging streams along east coast of Malay Peninsula, Burma, Borneo, and Sumatra.

Dipterocarpus vernicifluus (D. turbinatus)
(Fig. 102)

Local Names. Kajoe lilin, damar katja wai, lagan, meloewang, bambang, kenam (Sumatra); keroewing (Banka I., off S.E. Sumatra); kaladan (S.E. and central Borneo); palahlar (Sunda Is.); klalar (Java).

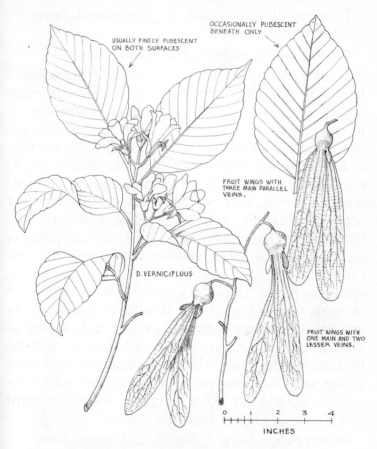

FIGURE 102. *Dipterocarpus vernicifluus*

Habit. Attains 150 to 200 ft. in height and 5 to 6 ft. in diameter, with about 100 ft. of clear length; trunk is straight and regular, without buttresses; young branchlets with fine gray or yellowish hairs.

Leaves. Simple, ovate, 5 to 7 in. long, leathery, with soft, fine hairs on both surfaces; petioles 2 in. long and bearing soft fine hairs.

Flowers. Large, white or rose-colored, borne in short axillary racemes.

Fruit. Small, globose, 2-winged.

Wood. Sapwood light, not sharply demarcated from the reddish-brown heartwood; growth rings not distinct; pores nearly all isolated, diffuse, small to large, some with tyloses and white deposits; parenchyma surrounding the pores and diffuse; resin canals generally isolated or in pairs, diffuse, small; rays fairly broad, few in number; grain crossed; texture coarse, dull in appearance, with resinous odor when freshly cut, but when dry without distinct taste or odor; heavy and hard; specific gravity, air-dry, 0.739 to 0.837, average 0.781; must be carefully seasoned as it is liable to warp and shrink excessively if not properly handled; moderately hard to work, takes a high polish, durable in interior work but not in contact with the ground unless treated with preservatives; used for posts, beams, rafters, flooring, bridge and wharf construction, including piling and telephone poles, when treated with preservatives, and for other purposes for which hard and heavy woods are required.

Occurrence. Burma; Sumatra, Borneo, Java.

SECTION OF FLOWER $\frac{2}{1}$

SECTION OF FRUIT

INCHES

FIGURE 103. *Dryobalanops aromatica*

283

Dryobalanops aromatica (Fig. 103)

Local Names. Kapur, kapur barus, Borneo camphor wood, kajoe kapoer (Malay States); hajoe hapoer (N.W. Sumatra, Battak country).

Habit. A large tree, may attain 10 ft. in diameter and often over 200 ft. in height with a clear length of 100 ft.; the trunk is straight with very little taper; buttresses are small; crown is dense and widespreading, occupying about ⅓ of the total height of the tree; the small twigs are slender and pendulous in large masses giving a distinctive appearance to the crown, recognizable at a considerable distance.

Leaves. Ovate or elliptical, sharply pointed, smooth, grayish, 1½ by 2 in. to 2½ by 4 in.; petiole 0.2 to 0.5 in. long; leaves vary considerably in size and give off a strong camphor odor when crushed.

Flowers. Borne in large clusters, very fragrant, white in color.

Fruit. Green or red, 1 by 1 in., winged.

Bark. Gray, yellow, or brown, ½ in. thick; young trees have smooth bark but the mature trees shed the outer bark in large, thin, irregular flakes, leaving an exposed surface which is purple in color; outer bark thin and corky; inner bark reddish-brown and fibrous, somewhat resinous and has a distinct camphor odor.

Wood. Sapwood white or yellowish, about 1 in. thick, sharply demarcated from brown or grayish-red heartwood; moderately hard and heavy; straight-grained; parenchyma scattered; rays medium in size, and evenly distributed; pores medium in size, diffuse with tyloses; may exude resin or oil from the resin ducts which are arranged in concentric lines; weight 38 to 43 lbs. per cu. ft., specific gravity 0.61 to 0.77; sapwood should be removed before the wood is used; has camphor odor when fresh-cut; logs are usually sound; has been used in nearly all types of construction except in contact with the ground; also used in small boat building, shelves, furniture, and shingles.

Occurrence. Very abundant, occurs with other trees from 200- to about 1,100-ft. elevation on well-drained soil; makes its best development on the slopes of low ridges, generally in well-drained soil; in the Malay States is generally found on the east side of the peninsula; never forms pure stands but may compose as much as 60 to 90 percent of the total volume; there are probably about 350,000 acres bearing this tree on the Malay Peninsula; also Borneo and Sumatra.

Hopea odorata (Fig. 104)

Local Names. Thingan, thitsingan (Burma); jangkang, merawan jangkang, damar poetih, dasal lanang, tjengal (Malayan); kedemoet (Banka I., off S.E. Sumatra); tjengal (Sunda Is.); djempina, kawang (Java); sanga (S.E. Borneo, Dayak country).

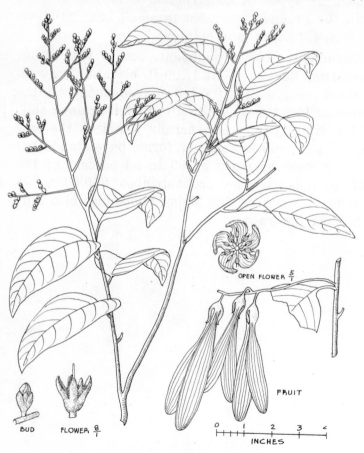

OPEN FLOWER $\frac{5}{1}$

FRUIT

BUD   FLOWER $\frac{8}{1}$

0   1   2   3   4
INCHES

FIGURE 104. *Hopea odorata*

Habit. Attains 4 ft. in diameter and 100 to 120 ft. in height, with a long symmetrical trunk.

Leaves. Large, simple, lanceolate.

Flowers. Small, white, quite fragrant.

Fruit. Small, with 2 wings, about 1½ in. long.

Bark. Gray to dark brown, with longitudinal furrows, inner bark yellow or red.

Wood. Dull grayish- or yellowish-brown; coarse-grained; pores filled with deposits; rays fine and inconspicuous; hard and heavy; generally durable and considered resistant to termites; has been used for boatbuilding, railroad ties, acid-resisting containers, and general construction.

Occurrence. Moist, tropical, rain forests; Burma, Borneo, Indo-China; similar allied species present in Malay Archipelago.

Hopea papuana

Local Names. — Koka-pilo-pilo (Doura, New Guinea.

Habit.—Attains 3 ft. in diameter and 60 ft. of clear length without buttresses.

Leaves.—Simple, alternate; petiole ½ in. long; blade 2 by 5 in. to 3 by 7 in., lanceolate, acuminate at tip, entire, glabrous, thin.

Fruit.—Ovoid, contains one seed, 3/16 in. long.

Bark.—Dark brown, scaly, ½ in. thick; inner bark white.

Wood.—Sapwood not demarcated from heartwood; resinous; cream to brown; rays 150 to 160 per in., yellow, sinuous around pores, appear as specks and lines on radial surface; pores 5,000 to 7,500 per sq. in., arranged in zones; parenchyma in very fine, concentric rings; specific gravity 0.882; cuts very hard; a good general construction wood.

Occurrence.—Northeast New Guinea, along the Vanapa River in Papua, foothills to about 2,000 ft.; probably also in Solomons.

FIGURE 105. –*Hopea philippensis*

Hopea philippensis (Fig. 105)

Local Names.—Baroho-puti, kubilisiau, magitarum, makatayring, makitarim, manggatarem, mapitarum, matikayram (Tayabas); baguntsan, gomerikgitik, pagakson, bagupsan, yakal (Camarines); gisok-gisok (Leyte, Negros Occidental, Zamboanga); gisok nga magisik (Bukidnon); gisok-malibato (Agusan); malimbato (Lanao); gisok (Zamboanga).

Habit.—Small tree attaining 24 in. in diameter and 40 ft. in height; trunk is short and attains about 25 ft. in length with buttresses.

Leaves.—Simple, alternate, 2 to 3 in. by 5 to 12 in.

Flowers.—Small, with 5 petals, borne in panicles.

Fruit.—Dry, winged.

Bark.—Dark brown to black, light brown when freshly cut, ½ in. thick, sheds large scaly patches; inner bark brown with pinkish tinge.

Wood.—Sapwood is thick, light colored, not sharply demarcated from the brown to reddish-brown heartwood; rays moderately narrow, few; pores isolated and in groups of 2 to 3, diffuse, fairly small, few to numerous, tyloses present; parenchyma extending between the rays in irregular bands, irregularly spaced; specific gravity, air-dry, 0.705 to 0.948, average 0.847; grain crossed, texture fine, without characteristic taste or odor, heavy, hard, subject to checking during seasoning, fairly hard to work, durable for interior use, moderately durable when exposed or in contact with the ground. Has been used for house corner posts and railroad ties.

Occurrence.—Phillipines; Luzon, Samar, Biliran, Leyte, Negros, Panay and Mindanao; has not been logged extensively in the past because of its small size; other species in this genus present in New Guinea.

Hopea pierrei (Fig. 106)

Habit. Attains 90 in. in diameter and 150 ft. in height with a clear length of 75 ft.; trunk is generally straight and cylindrical with only small buttresses but has stilt or prop roots projecting from the ground.

FLOWER $\frac{10}{1}$

0 1 2 3 4

INCHES

FIGURE 106. *Hopea pierrei*

291

Leaves. Simple, leathery, lanceolate, rounded at base, glabrous on both surfaces, 1 by 2½ in. to 2 by 5 in.; petiole ½ in. long.

Flowers. Borne in axillary and in terminal panicles, 1 to 2 in. long, flowers ¼ in. long.

Fruit. Ovoid, ½ in. long.

Bark. Thin and unfissured.

Wood. Sapwood 2 to 4 in. thick, light, not demarcated from the light-colored heartwood; growth rings indistinct; pores isolated and in groups, diffuse, most pores with tyloses; parenchyma around the pores and diffuse; resin ducts, in concentric rings, contain white resin; rays narrow, few in number; texture fine; grain crossed or wavy; glossy appearance, without characteristic taste or odor; heavy and very hard; specific gravity, air-dry, 0.867 to 0.999, average 0.918; difficult to work; durable when exposed to the weather and in contact with the ground; suitable for general construction, doors and windows, furniture, and agricultural implements.

Occurrence. Indo-China, Borneo.

FIGURE 107. *Isoptera borneensis*

Isoptera borneensis (Shorea seminis) (Fig. 107)

Local Names. Sengkawang, tengkawang, tengkawang pelepek, larat api (Malay States) ; balau (Dutch East Indies); tengkawang terindak, ramoehoen, tengkawang kalepek, tengkawang tanggoei (Borneo).

Habit. Attains 50 in. in diameter and 150 ft. in height with a clear length of 85 ft.; crown is open and widespread; trunk is straight and cylindrical, has small buttresses.

Leaves. Glabrous, lanceolate, light green on under side, 1 by 4 in. to 2 by 5 in.

Flowers. Borne in small panicles, yellow in color, have a vanilla odor.

Fruit. Globular, depressed, with short, thick, spreading or reflexed wings.

Bark. Gray or yellowish-gray, without fissures, somewhat powdery on the surface near the base of the trunk; 0.2 in. thick, sheds in thin, irregular flakes; inner bark thick, red, aromatic, astringent, and fibrous.

Wood. Sapwood 1 to 5 in. thick, light, not sharply demarcated from the yellowish-gray or dark brown heartwood; growth rings indistinct; pores solitary and in groups of 2 to 3, diffuse, most pores with tyloses; parenchyma surrounding the pores and diffuse; resin ducts in concentric arcs, very small, filled with white resin; rays narrow, few to fairly numerous; grain straight or crossed, texture fine; glossy in appearance, without distinct taste or odor; very heavy and hard; specific gravity, air-dry, 1.000 to 1.091, average 1.046; difficult to work but finishes well, very durable even when exposed or in contact

294

with the ground; suitable for all permanent construction where strength and durability are needed; has been used for wharves, bridges, and boatbuilding.

Occurrence. Occurs in the primary forests at low altitudes in alluvial soil or stream valleys in areas subject to periodic flooding, but makes its best development on better-drained sites, and has been planted up to 600-ft. elevation in Java and Sumatra; Malay Peninsula, Borneo, Java, and Sumatra.

Pentacme contorta (Fig. 108)

Local Names. White lauan (Trade).

Habit. A very tall, straight tree, attaining 120 ft. in height and 60 in. in diameter; with clear length of 40 to 80 ft.; trunk straight but with large buttresses.

INCHES

FIGURE 108. *Pentacme contorta*

Leaves. Simple, slightly leathery, broadly elliptical, apex blunt, base rounded, smooth, glabrous, 3 by 5 in. to 5 by 7 in.

Flowers. About 1 in. long, borne in few-flowered axillary panicles which are 2 to 5 in. long.

Fruit. Ovate, 1 in. long, smooth, glabrous.

Bark. Rough, dark-brown, inner bark thick and red, containing considerable tannin.

Wood. Sapwood 2 to 3 in. thick, not distinct from the light gray heartwood; growth rings indistinct; pores mainly isolated, diffuse, mostly with tyloses; parenchyma surrounding the pores and diffuse, not conspicuous; resin ducts in cencentric arcs, filled with white resin; rays narrow, grain crossed, giving a ribbon appearance on the radial surface; texture coarse with glossy appearance; without distinct taste or odor; light to fairly heavy; specific gravity, air-dry, 0.455 to 0.683, average 0.539; seasons well, with only a small amount of checking; works easily, takes a high finish; durable for interior work but not durable when exposed or in contact with the ground; used for cabinet work, boat planking, plywood, boxes and crates, mine timbers, and general construction.

Occurrence. Widely distributed in the forests at low altitudes; Java, Sumatra, Borneo, Malay Peninsula.

Pentacme siamensis (Fig. 109)

Habit. Attains 40 to 50 ft. in height; young branches thick, dark and glabrous.

Leaves. Simple, somewhat leathery, ovate or elliptical, both surfaces glabrous, 2 by 5 in. to 4 by 7 in.; petiole 1 in. long.

FLOWER $\frac{6}{1}$

FIGURE 109. *Pentacme siamensis*

Flowers. Borne in axillary panicles, 2 to 5 in. long, flowers 1 in. long.

Fruit. Ovate, glabrous, 1 in. long.

Wood. Very hard, heavy, strong and durable; specific gravity, air-dry, 0.95 to 1.12, average 0.99; suitable for general heavy construction.

Occurrence. Malay Peninsula; Siam, Indo-China.

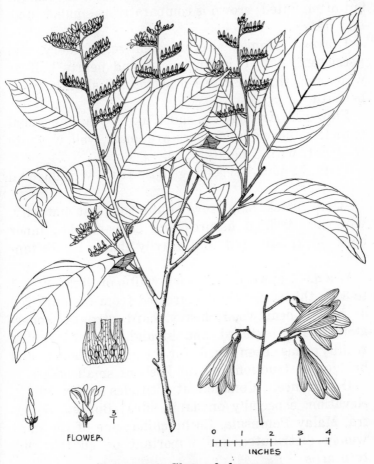

FLOWER

$\frac{3}{1}$

0 1 2 3 4
INCHES

FIGURE 110. *Shorea balangeran*

299

Shorea balangeran (Fig. 110)

Local Names. Belangiran (Malayan); melangir (Banka I., off S.E. Sumatra); kaweh, tomeh, mahambong, kahoi (Borneo).

Habit. A very large tree, often attains 150 ft. in height and 60 in. in diameter; the trunk is clear of branches for ⅔ of the total height and is straight but often fluted; crown is comparatively small, round, and dense.

Leaves. Simple, alternate, entire, leathery, and persistent, 3 to 6 in. in length and nearly half as wide, smooth, glossy green above and slightly paler beneath.

Flowers. Arranged in short, axillary and terminal panicles; individual flowers are small, yellow, quite fragrant, with 5 petals.

Fruit. Small, 1-seeded, globose fruit with unequal wings.

Bark. Thick, pale brown, quite rough at maturity, with longitudinal fissures and cross-checks; inner bark thick, quite red, and heavily charged with tannin.

Wood. Sapwood yellowish-white or light red, 1 to 3 in. thick, sharply demarcated from the dark red or brown heartwood; heavy, hard, strong; moderately coarse-textured and straight-grained; splits readily; has been used for beams in house and bridge construction and for keels of small boats.

Occurrence. Common at altitudes below 300-ft. elevation, especially on damp sites; Borneo, Sumatra, Malay Peninsula, Cochinchina; one of the most widely distributed and important of all the Dipterocarps.

MATURE FLOWER

0 1 2 3 4
INCHES

10

FLOWER WITH PETALS
AND SEPALS REMOVED

FIGURE 111. *Shorea cochinchinensis*

301

Shorea cochinchinensis (Fig. 111)

Local Names. Temak (Malay States); xen cat, xen, mu, dom propel ma sau (Siam, Cambodia, Cochinchina).

Habit. Attains 100 ft. in height and 3 ft. in diameter; trunk usually straight, cylindrical, and clear for about ½ of total height.

Leaves. Simple, leathery, may be glabrous or with fine hairs, elliptical or lanceolate, pointed at end and rounded at base, 2 by 4 in. to 3 by 7 in.; petiole ½ to 2 in. long; very young leaves purplish and with fine hairs.

Flowers. White, ¾ in. long; borne in loose axillary clusters, 4 to 5 in. long.

Fruit. A small, globose, leathery capsule, winged, with a single seed.

Bark. Thick, rough, and fissured, yields a resin-damar which is used as a substitute for pitch.

Wood. Yellow; cross-grained, fine- to coarse-textured, soft to very hard, moderately light to very heavy; growth rings not distinct; pores isolated and in groups, diffuse; parenchyma surrounding the pores; rays filled with white resin; resin ducts arranged in concentric arcs; specific gravity, air-dry, 0.58 to 0.66, average, 0.61; recommended for general construction work, particularly for beams, flooring, mine timbers, railroad ties, boat building, and all purposes for which a strong, durable wood is required.

Occurrence. Malay Peninsula, French Indo-China, Java, Siam, and Borneo.

FIGURE 112.—*Shorea guiso*

Shorea guiso (Fig. 112)

Local Names.—Guijo (Cagayan, Tayabas, Batangas, Rizal, Mindoro, Cebu, Negros, Cotabato, Davao, Zamboanga, Basilan); sarai, teka (Cagayan); barosingsing, lasilasan (Ilocos Norte, Mountain Province); pisek (Ilocos Norte, Ilocos Sur); mulauinaso (Abra); amtam, koriua, kurivet, kuribu, liamban (Isabela); karivat, kuriat (Nueva Vizcaya, Nueva Ecija); arimbokal, gisep, kaliot, pamayauasen (Pangasinan); gisok-pula, oaylayan, yamban-yamban (Zambales); taralai (Tarlac); yamban (Pangasinan, Nueva Ecija); giso (Bataan, Zambales, Camarines, Sorsogon, Leyte, Misamis); betik (Rizal, Laguna); doniri, gisik (Tayabas); dalinglingan (Batangas); gisok na apitungon, gisok na pula (Camarines); guijo colorado (Albay); bohukan, gisok (Sorsogon); ganganan, gisok madag, gisok nga pula (Leyte); gisok bayabason, gisok nga bayauason (Samar); bulog (Negros Occidental); red lauan (Lanao); linas (Cotabato); bagu, kongkong, malibato (Davao); giho blanco, dagindingan, kloang (Zamboanga); gisek (Cotabato, Basilan).

Habit.—A large tree attaining 90 in. in diameter with 45 to 75 ft. of main stem; trunk straight and cylindrical with large buttresses.

Leaves.—Simple, alternate, 1½ to 4 in. by 4 to 9 in., smooth.

Flowers.—Yellow, borne in axillary or terminal panicles, sweet odor.

Fruit. — Single seeded, and characteristically winged.

Bark.—2½ to 3 in. thick, light brown, sheds in scroll shaped or nearly rectangular patches; freshly exposed bark cinnamon brown; inner bark light reddish-brown and stringy texture.

304

Wood.—Sapwood 1 to 3 in. thick; heartwood reddish to brown; rays narrow, few to numerous, straight; pores isolated and in groups, diffuse, few to numerous, tyloses present; specific gravity, air-dry, 0.758 to 0.878, average 0.839; grain is crossed, texture fine, without distinct taste or odor, glossy appearance; seasons slowly and liable to split, warp and check if not properly seasoned; durable in interior work but only moderately so when exposed or in contact with the ground; suitable for general construction, beams, bridges and docks, furniture, frames of vehicles, frames of ships, and other purposes for which a strong wood is required.

Occurrence.—Philippines; widely distributed in Luzon, Mindoro, Panay, Negros, Masbate, Samar, Leyte, Mindanao, and Basilan; found in virgin forests at low and medium altitudes; fairly abundant; other species in this genus present in New Guinea.

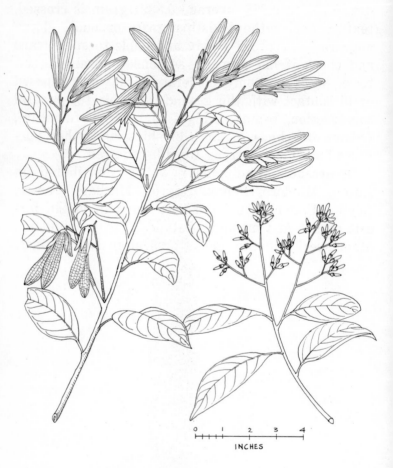

FIGURE 113. *Vatica astrotricha*

306

Vatica astrotricha (Fig. 113)

Local Names. Resok (Malay Peninsula); lau tau giam, lau tau trang, tra lac, chramas (Cochinchina).

Habit. Attains 80 to 100 ft. in height and 36 in. in diameter; trunk is straight and with only small buttresses; crown is dense.

Leaves. Simple, dull gray, leathery, with smooth margins, ovate to lanceolate, 1 by 2 in. to 2 by 5 in., both surfaces smooth.

Flowers. About ¾ in. long, borne in terminal and axillary panicles which are 2 to 4 in. long.

Fruit. A globose schizocarp, with 5 unequal wings.

Bark. Light-colored, thin, and unfissured; the inner bark usually yellow or brownish and resinous.

Wood. Sapwood yellowish and resinous, well demarcated from the light yellow heartwood; sapwood not considered durable; heartwood yellow when fresh but turns brownish upon exposure; grain straight; texture fine, glossy; without distinct taste or odor; very hard, heavy, and strong; growth rings not distinct; pores isolated, small; parenchyma diffuse; resin ducts filled with white resin; rays indistinct; members of this genus have been used for salt-water piling when treated with preservatives; it is suitable for all general construction purposes for which a hard, strong, durable wood is required.

Occurrence. Usually along ridges or low hills, from 700 to 2000 ft. in elevation; Malay Peninsula, Cochinchina, Borneo.

FIGURE 114.—*Vatica mangachapoi*

Vatica mangachapoi (Fig. 114)

Local Names.—Banik (Cagayan); adagan, kaliot, munchiat (Ilocos Norte); kalalinigin, labang (Ilocos Sur); asasin, salngen (La Union); aniga (Mountain Province); aningat, asip, bonga putian, tiranlai (Pangasinan); kairokan, karig, korigor, koring (Bataan); danggi, ititan (Laguna); patsahingin (Polillo); marig, paina, payina, yakal blanco (Tayabas); dagin, dagum (Camarines); tapurau (Albay); salong-salong (Sorsogon); bongoran, salngan (Samar); doro, saungsaungan (Leyte); tapulao (Capiz); bagosangan (Surigao); salong-salongan (Agusan); bagasusu, gisok (Lanao); apitong-blanco lutub, tampasak, tapitong (Zamboanga). This wood is sometimes sold in the market as "yakal blanco", meaning White Yakal.

Habit.—A medium sized tree to 35 in. in diameter with 30 to 45 ft. of main stem; trunk is straight with low buttresses.

Leaves.—Simple, alternate, leathery, 1½ to 2½ in. x 2 to 5 in.

Flowers.—Yellow, borne in terminal or axillary panicles.

Fruit.—Leathery or woody, winged, opens by 2 valves, and contains a single seed.

Bark.—¼ to ½ in. thick, outer bark light gray in color, freshly exposed bark brown to brownish-gray; sheds in scroll shaped pieces; inner bark light pink with brown flecks, hard and brittle.

Wood.—Sapwood 5 in. thick, sharply demarcated from the heartwood; heartwood is pale yellow when green, yellowish-brown when dry; rays moderately broad, few, lighter in color than surrounding tissue; pores nearly all isolated, diffuse, small, numerous, tyloses present; resin ducts diffuse, extremely small, filled with white resin; specific gravity air-dry 0.970; grain straight, texture fine, without distinctive taste or odor; glossy, very heavy, seasons well, is easy to work, takes high polish; heartwood very durable even when exposed or when in contact with the ground; sapwood is not durable. The thick sapwood should be removed and only the heartwood used. It is suitable for salt water piling, telephone poles, and other uses requiring a hard, durable wood.

Occurrence.—Philippines; Babuyan, Luzon, southward to Leyte, Samar and Mindanao; found in virgin forests at low and medium altitudes to 2,500 ft. elevation; is widely distributed but obtainable locally only in small quantities; other species in this genus present in New Guinea.

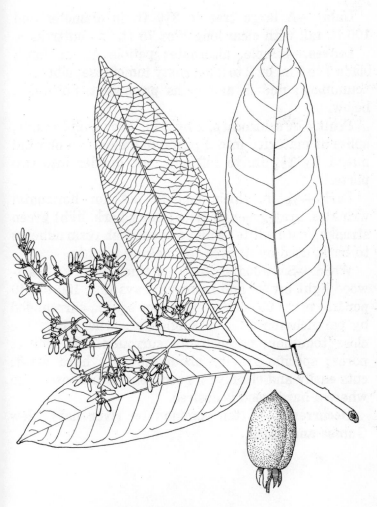

FIGURE 115.—*Vatica papuana.*

311

Vatica papuana (Fig. 115)

Local Names. — Kokolaka (Vailala), bou-ura (Keke); salo hiroe (Terrate); damar aloeng (Batjan).

Habit.—A large tree to 3½ ft. in diameter and 100 ft. tall with clear length of 75 ft.; no buttresses.

Leaves.—Simple, alternate; petiole ¾ in. long; blade 7 to 9 in. by 2 to 3 in., rusty tomentose; elliptical, acuminate; midrib and veins prominent, pubescent below.

Fruit.—A schizocarp, 1 by 2 in., brown and rough; splits at maturity into 3 parts and allows an obovoid nut, 1 by 1¼ in. to fall out; nut divides into two parts.

Bark.—¾ in. thick, smooth but for horizontal wrinkles, gray-green in color; inner bark, light green streaked with white; white or yellowish resin adheres to bark, used by natives for making torches.

Wood.—Sapwood about 5 in. thick, yellow; heartwood light brown and resinous; rays fine, 120 to 140 per in.; pores 20,000 to 30,000 per sq. in., surrounded by parenchyma cells, in single lines where rays are close together; parenchyma surround and connect pores; specific gravity about 0.673; a hard wood; cuts easily and cleanly; a good general purpose wood where a hard wood is desired.

Occurrence.—Often common on river flats, New Guinea and Papua.

FRUIT

0 1 2 3 4
INCHES

FIGURE 116. *Vatica rassak*

313

Vatica rassak (Fig. 116)

Local Names. Rasak danau, rasak natoei, rasak sabah (Borneo).

Habit. A large tree, attains 100 to 120 ft. in height and 3 ft. in diameter. All species are quite resinous.

Leaves. Simple, leathery, with smooth margins, very large, often 10 to 27 in. long and 3 to 6 in. wide.

Flowers. Yellow and arranged in terminal or axillary panicles.

Fruit. Dry, conical or globular, containing a single seed.

Bark. Thin, fairly smooth, light yellowish, only rarely shows longitudinal fissures, that of old trees usually turns dark.

Wood. The wood of all the species of *Vatica* is essentially alike. Sapwood often thick, white, and sharply demarcated from the heartwood which is hard, heavy, and straw-colored; often stains dark brown upon drying; like that of its allied species, the wood is employed extensively for construction purposes.

Occurrence. Reported to occur on most of the main islands; Borneo and Indo-China.

314

Flacourtiaceae

(Flacourtia Family)

Mostly trees and shrubs, natives of the tropics; leaves alternate, entire or toothed; a few species afford edible fruits, while still others are sources of tannins, drugs, oils, and resins.

FIGURE 117. *Homalium bracteatum*

Homalium bracteatum (Fig. 117)

Habit. A small tree, attaining 24 in. in diameter and 40 ft. in height.

Leaves. Simple, alternate, smooth, with wavy margins, 1½ by 3 in. to 6 by 13 in.

Flowers. Small, white, numerous, borne in terminal racemes.

Fruit. A small, dry, one-celled capsule, opens by 3 valves and contains several seeds.

Bark. About ½ in. thick, gray to brown, slightly uneven surface, sometimes with vertical lines.

Wood. Light yellow to orange when fresh, turning reddish-brown with age; growth rings indistinct; rays narrow; pores in groups of 2 to 3, diffuse, small, numerous, parenchyma indistinct; grain straight or slightly crossed, texture fine; heavy, hard and strong; suitable for general construction.

Occurrence. Widely distributed in virgin forests at low altitudes; many other species in this genus present in the region, extending from Borneo and Siam to Southern China and Formosa.

FIGURE 118.—*Homalium pachyphyllum.*

Homalium pachyphyllum (Fig. 118)

Local Names.—Malasa (Nakanai, New Britain), kavea (Vailala).

Habit.—Large tree, to 3 ft. in diameter and 110 ft. in height with 80 ft. of clear length; narrow buttresses up to 8 ft.

Leaves.—Simple, alternate; petiole ⅜ to ½ in. long, twisted; blade 6 to 9 in. by 3 to 5 in., oval or obovate, smooth, slightly leathery; midrib and veins regular and prominent.

Flowers.—Borne in axillary panicles, 11 in. long; flowers yellow-green, solitary or in pairs; peduncle ⅛ in. long.

Fruit.—A capsule.

Bark.—Gray-brown, ⅝ in. thick, generally smooth; inner bark yellow-brown.

Wood.—Orange to brown; sapwood not demarcated from heartwood; rays 290 to 330 per in., both coarse and fine, sinuous; pores 12,000 to 15,000 per sq. in., evenly distributed; specific gravity 0.978; cuts medium hard; durable in the ground; used as an oar wood in New Britain and for house posts in Papua; woods of other species of this genus in Philippines resistant to teredo and termites and are used for salt water piling, shipbuilding, railroad ties, house construction, etc.

Occurrence.—New Guinea and Bismarck Archipelago, on alluvial flats and foothills.

Datiscaceae

(Bastard Hemp Family)

Several species of trees and some herbs widely scattered over North America, northern India, Siberia, and the Indian Archipelago. They contain bitter and purgative qualities and a yellow dyestuff in the inner bark.

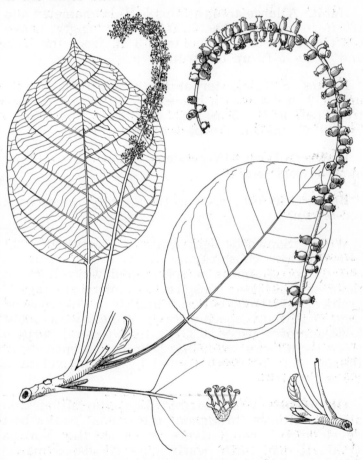

FIGURE 119. *Octomeles sumatrana*

Octomeles sumatrana (Fig. 119)

Local Names. Binoewang (North Sumatra, Battak country); benoewang (Malayan). New Guinea: kakerim (Yabim, Markham River coast); usu (Yalu, Lower Markham Valley); erima (Rabaul); benumba (Buna, Binendele); ilimo (Motu and Suku); ipa (Evara).

Habit. A large tree; attains 5 ft. in diameter and 180 ft. in height, with 100 ft. of clear length; heavy buttresses which often extend 8 ft. from the base and 12 to 15 ft. up the trunk.

Leaves. Simple, alternate; on young trees, petiole up to 12 in. long with blade 9 by 12 in.; on mature trees, petiole 2 to 5 in. long with blade 2 by 5 in. to 7 by 9 in.; midrib and base of veins brown.

Flowers. Borne in pendent spikes, 12 to 18 in. long, flowers sessile.

Bark. Gray-brown, 1 in. thick, scaly; inner bark red-brown.

Wood. Sapwood light yellow, heartwood light brown; rays conspicuous, dark brown, sinuous around pores, appear as specks and wavy lines on radial surface; pores conspicuous, numerous; straight-grained; heartwood cuts soft and clean but sapwood somewhat wooly; specific gravity of heartwood about 0.368 and of sapwood, 0.337; a light general purpose wood for interior work; has been cut extensively in Papua, and has been planted by the natives as a canoe-log tree.

Occurrence. Well distributed on alluvial flats and at low altitudes throughout the region; makes best development along rivers such as the Vanapa (Papua); may form nearly pure stands; Sumatra; Borneo; on New Britain, it occurs in quantity in association with *Eucalyptus deglupta*.

Thymeliaceae

(Mezereum Family)

Trees, shrubs, or sometimes herbs; leaves alternate, smooth-margined, leathery; flowers axillary or terminal; fruit sub-globose, 1-seeded, fleshy, with thin outer coating. The representatives occur in the temperate and tropical parts of the world.

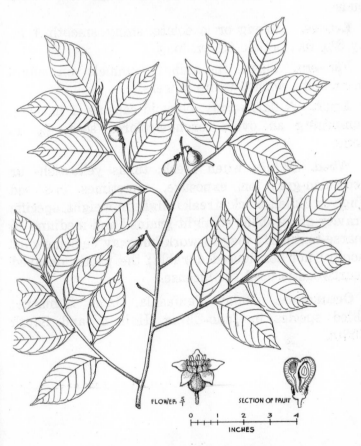

FLOWER $\frac{5}{1}$ SECTION OF FRUIT

FIGURE 120. *Aquilaria malaccensis*

Aquilaria malaccensis (Fig. 120)

Local Names. Karas, tuikaras, tangkaras, tabak (sakai fide skeat), gaharu (Malay Peninsula); alim (Battak country, N.W. Sumatra); kepang (Billiton I., off S.E. Sumatra); kareh (W. central Sumatra); halim (S.E. Sumatra, Lampong).

Habit. Attains 60 to 80 ft. in height; has silky buds.

Leaves. Oblong or laceolate, shiny, smooth, 1 in. by 3¼ in.; petiole 0.1 in. long.

Flowers. Borne in axillary umbels on short branchlets, with 6 white flowers.

Fruit. A flat, woody, obovoid capsule, 1 in. long, containing an ovoid, orange-colored seed, ¼ in. long.

Wood. White when fresh, turns yellowish- or brownish-gray on exposure, sometimes has red tinge or bluish-black streaks; light in weight, specific gravity about 0.35; straight-grained and medium- to coarse-textured; easy to work but may be somewhat woolly; not considered durable; the partly decayed heartwood is used for incense.

Occurrence. Malay Peninsula, Java, Sumatra; allied species in Indo-China, Hainan, and South China.

Lythraceae

(Loosestrife Family)

Trees and shrubs often with square branches and with opposite, alternate, or whorled and entire leaves. Plants are chiefly tropical, but some are found in the temperate zones. Fruit is capsular, dry, and dehiscent, with many seeds. A number of the plants yield tannins, dyes, oils, and bitter principles.

FIGURE 121. *Lagerstroemia speciosa*

Lagerstroemia speciosa (Fig. 121)

Local Names. Boengoer, boengoer bener (Malayan); boengoer koewat, boengoer tekoejoeng (Sumatra); boengoer (Sunda Is.); ketangi, laban, woengoe (Java); bhoengor (Madura). Philippines: nabulong, tabangao, tanbangau (Cagayan); banaba (Ilocos Norte, Ilocos Sur, Abra, La Union, Pangasinan, Bulacan, Bataan, Mindoro, Palawan, Antique, Negros, Davao); arioag, makabalo (Pangasinan); mitla (Tarlac); banangpulo (Tayabas); panthahaun (Camarines); agupanga (Marinduque); pamalasagon (Leyte); pamalauagon, pamarauagon (Samar, Leyte); kau-ilan (Iloilo); manaba (Capiz); parasabukung (Misamis); batiladhan (Lanao); abuk (Agusan, Zamboanga).

Habit. Medium-sized tree attaining 10 in. in diameter and 75 ft. in height; trunk usually short, irregularly shaped, and with only small buttresses.

Leaves. Simple, opposite, ovate, sharply pointed, entire margins, thin, smooth; petiole ¼ in. long; blade 3 by 4 in.

Flowers. Large, pink or purplish; borne in terminal panicles.

Fruit. A dry capsule, about ¾ in. in length, with 3 to 6 cells containing numerous small winged seeds.

Bark. About 3 in. thick, gray to brown, with yellowish tint, fine vertical lines, may be scaly; inner bark turns purple on exposure.

Wood. Sapwood 2 to 3 in. thick, not sharply demarcated from the reddish-brown heartwood; rays narrow, numerous, lighter than surrounding tissue; pores isolated, arranged in zones, small to large, few in number, tyloses present in all pores; parenchyma surrounding the pores with wing-like lateral extensions which occasionally join with adjacent ones; growth rings distinct; specific gravity air-dry, 0.670; grain straight, sometimes wavy; texture fine to coarse; glossy; without distinct taste or odor; heavy, hard and strong; seasons well; shrinks and warps very little; easy to work and takes a high finish; durable when exposed or in contact with the ground; suitable for ship building, flooring, interior finish, furniture and cabinet work; has been extensively used for house posts.

Occurrence. Throughout the region; scattered along streams in open localities and in the second-growth forests; not available in large quantities; often cultivated as an ornamental tree because of its showy purple flowers; Burma, Malay Peninsula, Indo- China; in the Philippines, found on Bataan Island and northern Luzon to Palawan, Mindanao and the Sulu Archipelago; similar species of the genus present throughout the region.

Sonneratiaceae

(Sonneratia Family)

Trees and shrubs many of which were formerly grouped in the myrtle family; its members are distributed widely throughout the western Pacific region; grow chiefly just back of the mangrove swamps; only a few species of any importance. Trees medium-sized to tall; generally with straight, regular boles; the roots develop knees or air roots which are used locally as substitutes for cork.

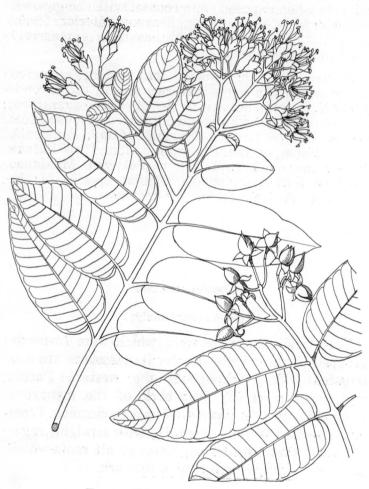

FIGURE 122. *Duabanga moluccana*

Duabanga moluccana (Fig. 122)

Local Names. Takir (Java); taker (Madura); kadjimas (Bali); radjoemas (Lombok); raba, ranga (N. Halmahera); ole (Ternate); kora (Tidore). Philippines: arek, arik (Cagayan, Pangasinan); bukag, kadig, kadir (Cagayan, Ilocos Norte, Ilocos Sur, Mountain Province); loktob (Cagayan, Tabayas, Laguna, Mindoro, Albay, Zamboanga, La Union); tarig (Isabela, Mountain Province); dapul (Mountain Province); bayukan (Nueva Vizcaya); malailangilang (Nueva Ecija); kadel, kadil (Tayabas); banalang-bugtong, darai, mala-palikpik (Rizal); anaang, haman (Catanduanes); adha, biguang, karauan (Camarines); ilo-ilo (Capiz); dahi (Negros Occidental, Misamis, Davao); tikatan (Cotabato); lamud (Cotabato, Davao); laton (Zamboanga).

Habit. Attains 45 in. in diameter and 75 ft. in height, with a main stem of 45 ft.; trunk is straight but short.

Leaves. Simple, opposite, 2 by 8 in. to 3 by 13 in., leathery, heart-shaped; short petioles.

Flowers. Pale greenish-yellow, borne in terminal cymes.

Fruit. A capsule, with numerous small seeds.

Wood. Sapwood 3 to 4 in. thick, not sharply demarcated from the reddish-brown heartwood; rays narrow, numerous; pores generally in pairs, diffuse, small to large, tyloses generally present; parenchyma in narrow bands; specific gravity, air-dry, 0.394; grain crossed, texture coarse; without distinct taste or odor; light, soft and weak; seasons well and is easy to work; not durable when exposed or in contact with the ground; used for buoyancy in the rafting of heavy logs, for fish net floats, dugout canoes, and light temporary construction; suitable for veneer and plywood.

Occurrence. In forests along streams at low and medium altitudes up to 3,600 ft.; considerable quantities available; Malay Archipelago, Celebes, Moluccas and New Guinea; in Philippines, on Luzon, Mindoro, Palawan, Leyte, Panay, Negros and Mindanao.

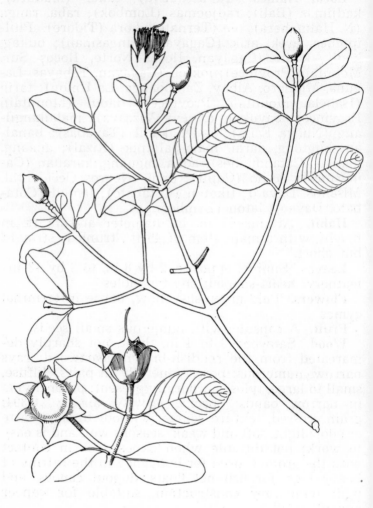

FIGURE 123. *Sonneratia caseolaris*

Sonneratia caseolaris (S. alba) (Fig. 123)

Local Names. Gedabu, pepat, perepat (Malayan).

Habit. Large tree, to 4½ ft. in diameter and 90 ft. in height, with 60 ft. of clear length; without buttresses but produces a large number of aerial roots.

Leaves. Simple, opposite, petiole ¼ in. long; blade 1 by 1 in. to 5 by 6 in., almost circular or elliptical, very leathery, venation indistinct, smooth-surfaced.

Flowers. Borne terminal and solitary.

Bark. Gray-brown, ⅛ in. thick, with flat longitudinal ridges; inner bark red-brown.

Wood. Yellow to deep pink; sapwood not differentiated from heart-wood; rays 360 per in., sinuous, not prominent on radial surface; pores 12,000 to 14,000 per sq. in., evenly distributed; grain not prominent; specific gravity 0.593; cuts fairly hard; considered resistant to marine borers; suitable for salt-water construction.

Occurrence. Occurs on landward side of mangrove swamps or of open beaches but within influence of brackish water; throughout the region.

Crypteroniaceae
(Crypteronia Family)

Trees with 4-angled branches and with opposite and entire leaves. Fruit is a 2-celled, dehiscent capsule with numerous small seeds. In many other respects similar to those of the plants of the Loosestrife and Sonneratia families. The type genus *Crypteronia* is confined to tropical Asia.

FIGURE 124. *Crypteronia paniculata.*

Cypteronia panioculata (Fig. 124)

Local Names. Buah babi, bekoi, berkol, bekwoi, rupal (Malay Peninsula); ki banen (Sunda Is.); kajoe tjeleng (Java). Philippines; agidai (Cagayan); kodai, kudai, ladau (Mountain Province); barabok, booken (Ilocos Sur); baruga (Abra); baliuag (Nueva Ecija); malabiong (Zambales); bitok (Bulacan); bongganii, bugna, tua, tualin (Rizal); malabayabas (Bataan); tiaui (Laguna); tuug (Marinduque, Negros).

Habit. Attains 24 in. in diameter and about 25 ft. of clear length; trunk cylindrical.

Leaves. Simple, opposite, entire.

Flowers. Small, white or greenish, borne in racemes.

Fruit. A small dry capsule.

Wood. Sapwood thin, light red, not sharply demarcated from the reddish to grayish-brown heartwood; rays narrow, very numerous; pores mostly in groups of 2 to 4, small, numerous; gum ducts dark brown, distinctly visible on tangential surface, filled with dark gummy deposits; grain slightly crossed, texture fine; without distinct odor but taste is astringent; glossy; moderately hard, heavy, and tough; seasons well and works well; durability in exposed situations is not known; has been used for general construction, mainly for flooring.

Occurrence. Throughout the region; common at low and medium altitudes; supply is limited; Burma to Indo-China and Malay Archipelago.

Lecythidaceae

(Brazil Nut Family)

The leaves of the trees in this family are simple and alternate. The flowers are usually large and showy, and the fruits are characteristically hard, woody, often large. This family produces the well-known Brazil nuts in the genus *Bertholletia*.

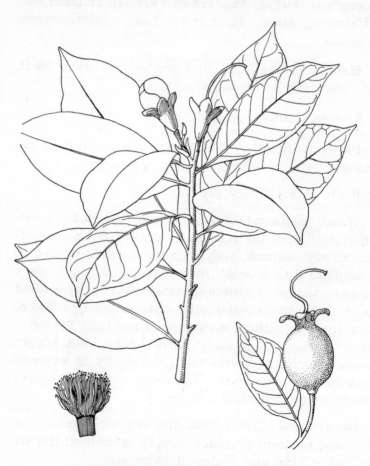

FIGURE 125.–*Planchonia papuana.*

Planchonia timorensis (see Fig. 125 for similar species)

Local Names.—Biribiri (Buna), aruntem (Yalu, Lower Markham Valley), kaeda (Suku), paira (Evara), puri-iki (Vailala); dingkaeleng (Sangir); ipil, intjalen, achlem (N. Celebes); poetjat sasa (Boegina).

Habit.—A large tree, to 3 ft. in diameter and 120 ft. in height with 60 ft. of clear length; without buttresses or flanges.

Leaves.—Simple, alternate, pinnate venation, 6 by 4 in., obovate, edges finely toothed, smooth, thin.

Flowers.—Large, conspicuous, pale white.

Fruit.—Fleshy, green in color 2 by 3 in.; has large number 3-sided seeds.

Bark.—Red-brown, rough and fibrous, ½ in. thick; inner bark red-brown; bark of young trees used by natives as rough cordage.

Wood.—Sapwood pale yellow, 3 to 4 in. thick; heartwood red-brown; rays 280 to 300 per in.; pores conspicuous, 3,000 to 3,500 per sq. in. evenly distributed; parenchyma surrounds pores, also in thin lines between rays; grain inconspicuous; specific gravity 0.884; cuts hard; a heavy, strong wood.

Occurrence.—Found in vicinity Vanapa (Papua), New Guinea, Bismarcks and Solomons; coastal lowlands and low ridges.

Rhizophoraceae

(Mangrove Family)

Trees and shrubs distributed in narrow belts along the seashore and in brackish swamps generally throughout the tropics; the species are mostly maritime trees commonly known as mangrove; leaves opposite, leathery, thickish, and entire; bark thick, hard, and brittle; wood and inner bark dark red and heavily charged with tannin.

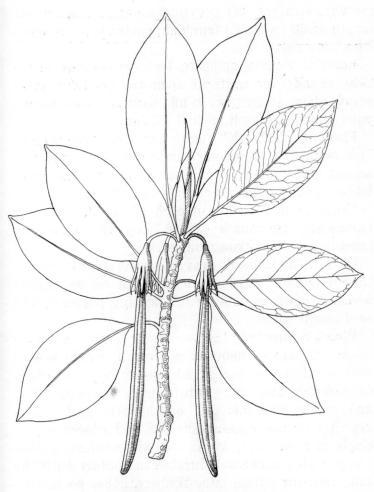

FIGURE **126.** *Bruguiera conjugata*

Bruguiera conjugata (B. gymnorhiza) (Fig. 126)

Habit. A medium-sized tree attaining a height of 80 ft. and a diameter of 30 to 36 in.; the trunk is regular, straight, often cylindrical and has a clear length of 36 to 45 ft.; trunk supported by characteristic prop roots.

Leaves. Simple, opposite, leathery, ovate or elliptical, rounded or acute at apex and gradually narrowed at base, dark green and usually glossy above, paler beneath, 2 by 3 in. to 3 by 5 in.

Flowers. Yellowish, light cream-colored, or reddish, with 5 to 13 oblong petals, each cleft into two segments, leathery, woolly at the margin, and so folded that each petal conceals two stamens.

Fruit. The 2 seeds, in each of the 2 to 4 compartments, germinate before they fall from the branch, as in the true mangroves.

Bark. Thick, hard, grayish, fairly smooth; inner bark red and heavily charged with an astringent which is used extensively for tanning purposes and as a black dye.

Wood. Sapwood light-colored, about one inch thick, not sharply demarcated from the light brown heartwood which turns reddish-brown upon exposure to light and air; grain is straight; texture fine, and luster medium; one of the strongest woods growing in the region; shrinks and checks excessively in seasoning; works well and assumes a relatively high polish; not durable in contact with the soil; used for piling, mine timbers, house posts, furniture, and for fuel and charcoal.

Occurrence. Generally throughout the region along the shores of the islands; gregarious in mangrove swamps; the supply is abundant.

336

Rhizophora mucronata (Fig. 127)

Local Names. Bakau belukap, bakau jangkar, bakau kurap, belukap, bakau itam, bakau korap, bakau merah (Malay Peninsula) ; bangka itam, bangka oe (N.W. Sumatra, Achin country) ; dongoh korap (Simaloe I., off N.W. Sumatra) ; bako, djangkar

FIGURE 127. *Rhizophora mucronata*

Habit. Attains a diameter of 2 ft. and a height of 100 ft.; has characteristic prop roots.

Leaves. Simple, alternate; blade 2 by 4 in. to 3 by 7 in., elliptical, glabrous, leathery, somewhat translucent, venation distinct; petiole 1 to 2 in. long.

Flowers. Waxy appearance, usually greenish.

Fruit. Small, ovoid; seed germinates while fruit still on the tree developing a root about a foot long before falling from the tree.

Bark. About ½ in. thick; gray, rough, and ridged; inner bark red, faintly streaked with yellow.

Wood. Sapwood yellow, not sharply demarcated from reddish-brown heartwood; rays 170 per in., often in large sweeping curves, appear on radial surface as wavy bands and streaks; pores 10,000 per sq. in., very evenly distributed; specific gravity 0.995; with attractive figure on quarter grain; durable in salt water because of resistance to toredo; is used for piles and for framework of native houses.

Occurrence. One of the principal trees of mangrove swamp formation throughout the region.

Combretaceae

(Myrobalan Family)

227. Trees and shrubs indigenous to parts of tropical Asia, Africa and America. All parts of the plants contain astringent qualities; some species produce commercially important wood; leaves alternate or opposite, and entire; fruit of some species astringent and known by the name myrobalans produced chiefly by *Termimalia bellerica* and *T. chebula;* the bark of many species is used for tanning.

FIGURE 128.—*Terminalia brassii.*

Terminalia brassii (Fig. 128)

Habit.—A large tree with buttressed trunk; may dominate the associated species.

Leaves.—Simple, alternate, leathery.

Flowers.—Small, born in spikes.

Fruit.—Winged, unlike that of *T. catappoides* which is unwinged.

Wood.—Light sapwood not sharply demarcated from the darker heartwood; pores are isolated and in groups, few in number; growth rings not pronounced; grain slightly crossed; texture fine to moderately coarse; without distinctive odor or taste.

Occurrence.—Has been collected on San Cristobal I. and Ysabel I. and is considered one of the best timber trees in the Solomons. Occurs on coastal slopes and river flats.

Terminalia calamansanai (Fig.129)

Local Names.—Dalupit (Cagayan) ; anarep (Ilocos Norte, Ilocos Sur) ; pangalusiten (Abra) ; saket (Mountain Province) ; kalamansali, sakat (Nueva Ecija, Zambales) ; subo-subo (Zambales) ; dikang (Pampanga) ; mabantut, pantol (Bataan) ; bunlos (Rizal) ; kalumpit, malakalumpit (Bataan, Tayabas) ; magtalisai (Masbate) ; burauis, samburagat (Palawan) ; bankalanag (Antique) ; taya-taya (Iloilo) ; saplid, yangkug, lumanog (Surigao) ; langkog (Agusan) ; talisai (Cotabato) ; salisai (Lanao).

Habit.—Attains a diameter of 40 in. with a clear length of 25-to 35 ft.; fairly large buttresses.

Leaves.—Simple, elliptical, sharply pointed, 1½ by 4 in. on short petioles.

Flowers.—Borne in racemes, small, with five petals, on 1-inch peduncles.

Fruit.—Flattened, about 1 in. long, with two broad lateral wings.

Wood.—Sapwood not sharply demarcated from the heartwood; the heartwood turns from a light yellow when fresh to tan when dry; growth rings not distinct, marked by parenchyma; rays narrow, scarcely visible, numerous; pores in groups, radially arranged, diffuse, connected by parenchyma, small to large, few in number, occasionally have reddish-brown deposits; specific gravity, air-dry, 0.654; grains slightly crossed, often wavy; texture coarse, glossy, without distinct taste or odor, heavy, hard, strong, seasons well with very little difficulty, is easy to work, durable for interior use but perishable when exposed or in contact with the ground; has been little used in the past because of its lack of durability.

Occurrence.—Philippines; Babuyan, northern Luzon, Mindanao and Palawan; widely distributed in

341

the virgin forests but is not abundant; other species in the genus are present throughout the region.

FIGURE 129.–*Terminalia calamansanai*

Terminalia catappoides (see Fig. 130 for similar species)

Local Names.—Indian almond. Katapang (Ambon); salrise (Sangir); tarisei, doempajang (Celebes); wew (Kai I.); sadina, sarisa (W. Ceram); sertalo, sirisa (S. Ceram); sarisa-lo, sirisal (Oeliaser); lisa (Boeroe); tasi (Soela I.); klis (S. Halmahera); kalis, kris (W. New Guinea); ngoesoe, tiliho (N. Halmahera); ngoesoe (Ternate, Tidore); kauou-ya (Buna); okaka (Suku); Talisay (Philippines); yoru (Vailala).

Habit.—A large tree, to 5 ft. in diameter and over 130 ft. in height with a clear length of 80 ft.; heavy buttresses to 10 ft.; leafless for about a month during the dry season.

Leaves.—In groups at ends of branches; simple, alternate, petiole ¼ in. long, blade 10 to 14 in. by 4 to 5 in., obovate, blunt-pointed; glabrous, leathery.

Flowers.—Borne in pendent spikes, to 24 in. long, attached at leaf axile; bears large numbers of single flowers; peduncle ¼ in. long.

Fruit.—A hard corrugated nut, 3 by 1¾ in.; kernel ⅝ by ¼ in.

Bark.—Brown, ½ in. thick, has deep longitudinal lines; inner bark red with white streaks.

Wood.—Sapwood pale yellow, not clearly demarcated from dark brown heartwood; rays 125 to 130 per in., fine or coarse, yellowish-brown in color, sinuous around pores, appear as small speaks on radial surface; pores conspicuous, 2,500 per sq. in., evenly distributed; specific gravity 0.642; cuts hard; a good hard general utility wood.

Occurrence.—Of common occurrence in beach region of Philippines and in Papua from coast to 1,000 ft.; range extends into Northeast New Guinea; there are several other species of this genus in the **Bismarcks** and Solomons.

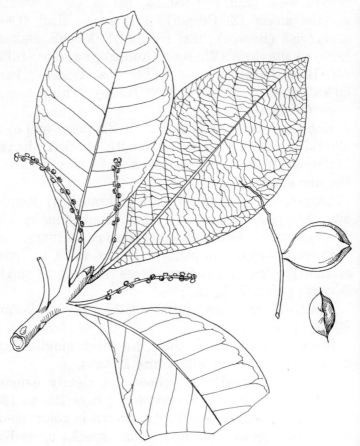

FIGURE 130.—*Terminalia catappa*

FIGURE 131. *Terminalia edulis*

345

Terminalia edulis (Fig. 131)

Local Names. Djaha benti, gamprit, kloempit, kloemprit, seloemprit (Java); klompek (Madura); kadjoe tandoe, kaloempit (Kangeang I., off N.E. Java); kloemprit, koenjit-koenjit (Bali). Philippines: alupi, kalupi, kalupit, kalusit, lauang (Cagayan); anagep (Cagayan, Mountain Province, Ilocos Sur); kaluatit (Cagayan Mountain Province, Nueva Vizcaya); ambobok, ambobonot (Isabela); sakat (Pampanga, Laguna); galamayon, gayumayen (Zambales); dalinsi (Tayabas, Bataan); bisal, kalosit (Bulacan); kalamansanai (Rizal); balisayin, dalasa, dumonsil, malagalis (Mindoro); tina (Camarines Norte); dalinsan kalamagon, tangal (Camarines Sur); kalimingog, kalumongog (Sorsogon, Masbate, Samar); magtalisai (Sorsogon, Masbate); lumangog (Leyte, Iloilo); tayataya (Iloilo); kalmagon (Samar); balisayon (Negros Occidental); kamaris (Palawan); bulao (Zamboanga).

Habit. Attains 50 in. in diameter with 30 to 35 ft. of main stem; trunk is straight and has small buttresses.

Leaves. Simple, alternate, smooth, loosely bunched at ends of twigs, 1 by 2 in. to 3 by 7 in.

Flowers. Small, with 5 petals, borne in elongated spikes.

Fruit. Ovoid, 1 in. long or less, somewhat compressed, with only one seed.

Bark. About ½ in. thick, brownish-black, irregularly ridged, scaly on old trees; inner bark yellowish, with watery sap.

Wood. Sapwood thick, yellowish, not sharply demarcated from the light to reddish-brown heartwood; rays narrow, irregularly spaced, fairly numerous, lighter than surrounding tissue; pores generally isolated, irregularly distributed, small to large, few in number, small amount of tyloses present; parenchyma surrounding the pores, also diffuse; growth rings not distinct, marked by zones of porous and less porous wood, may be marked by terminal parenchyma; specific gravity, air-dry, 0.545 to 0.620, average, 0.598; grain slightly crossed, may be curly or wavy; texture coarse; glossy; without distinct taste or odor; light to heavy; strong and hard; seasons well and takes a high finish; durable for interior work but perishable when exposed or in contact with the ground; suitable for ship planking, general construction, furniture, and cabinet making.

Occurrence. Widely distributed; found in open portions of the Dipterocarp forests at low and medium altitudes; frequent, but not abundant; Borneo, Java; in Philippines, from northern Luzon to Mindanao and Palawan; other species in the genus present in the region.

Terminalia foveolata

Local Names.—Kovo (Vailala), koivai-a (Evara).

Habit.—A large tree to 60 in. in diameter and 120 ft. in height with 90 ft. of main stem; very heavily buttressed to 15 ft. up the trunk.

Leaves.—Simple, alternate; petiole ½ in. long, blade 2 in. to 3½ in. x 2 in. to 4½ in.; elliptical to ovate, sharply pointed, thin and glabrous.

Flowers.—Small, green, borne in a spike at axils of leaves.

Fruit.—A drupe, somewhat flattened, with a single seed.

Bark.—Brown, ¾ in. thick, scaly, with longitudinal lines; inner bark purplish brown.

Wood.—Sapwood pale yellow, 1 in. thick; heartwood brown; rays reddish-brown, sinuous around pores or broken by pores; appear as minute specks on the radial surface; pores very conspicuous, occur singly, very numerous; parenchyma surround the pores; specific gravity, air-dry, 0.545; cuts soft and clean, works easily; the large pores make it possible to blow through it longitudinally; fairly hard.

Occurrence.—New Guinea.

Myrtaceae

(Myrtle Family)

Trees and shrubs of the temperate and tropical parts of both hemispheres, usually distinguished by their aromatic or pungent properties (essential oils) in their entire, opposite, and gland-dotted leaves; fruit dry or fleshy; flowers mostly 4-parted.

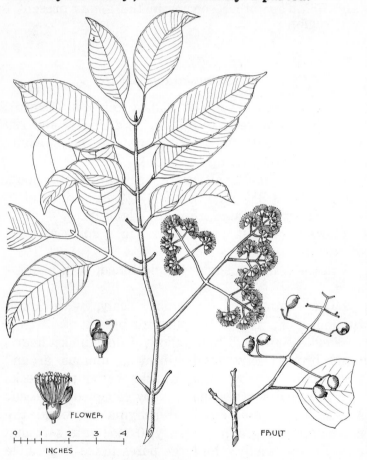

FLOWER

FRUIT

0 1 2 3 4
INCHES

FIGURE 136. *Syzygium cumini*

348

Fᴄᴜʀᴇ 132.—*Eucalyptus deglupta.*

Eucalyptus deglupta (Fig. 132)

Local Names.—Komo (Nakenai), Kamarere (Rabaul).

Habit.—A very large tree, to 7 ft. in diameter and 230 ft. in height with 150 ft. of clear length.

Leaves.—Simple, alternate; petiole ½ to ¾ in. long and twisted; blade 3 to 6 in. by 2 to 3 in.; lanceolate; acuminate, slightly leathery; aromatic when crushed. Twigs are rectangular in cross-section and grooved.

Flowers.—Numerous, white, borne in both axial and terminal panicles; central axis to 4 in. long, bearing groups of flowers on pedicels which shorten base to tip of the panicle.

Fruit.—Capsule with exserted valves; ⅛ in. in diameter.

Bark.—Generally under ¼ in. thick; peels off all year round in thin paper ribbons; freshly exposed surface is bright green which gradually changes through blue to purple, and finally to a brick-red; inner bark is white.

Wood.—Sapwood 1 to 1½ in. thick, white in color; heartwood reddish-brown; rays fine, 290-300 per in.; pores 4,000 per sq. in., visible due to surrounding parenchyma cells; parenchyma about 300 per in. in fine lines; specific gravity about 0.834; a hard, strong general utility wood, works up well.

Occurrence.—Confined to the rain forest formation. Forms almost pure stands of limited extent on alluvial areas, many scattered occurrences at low elevations near coast on New Britain; largest stands are on Powell and Henry Reid rivers flowing into Wide Bay, on the Toreo River flowing into Open Bay and at Korindal. There has been some logging in the principal stands. Known to occur also in the mountains of the southeast end of Northeast New Guinea, Celebes, Moluccas, and on Mindanao.

FIGURE 133.—*Eucalyptus tereticornis.*

Eucalyptus tereticornis (Fig. 133)

Local Names.—Blue gum, red gum (Australia).

Habit.—Attains 2 ft. in diameter and 80 ft. in height.

Bark.—Dark gray, rough and furrowed; on upper trunk and branches smooth and blue gray; peels off in long strips.

Wood.—Reddish in color, hard and heavy.

Occurrence.—Papua; on ridges west of Fly River in the dry lowlands and at elevation of about 1,000 ft. and above in the Port Moresby dry belt; there are several other tree species in the genus which are abundant in the dry regions.

FIGURE 134.–*Melaleuca leucadendron.*

Melaleuca leucadendron (Fig. 134)

Local Names.—Tea tree, paper bark. Gelam, kajoe poetih, kajoe gelang (Malayan); baroe galang (Makassar); waroe gelang (Boegina); iren, sakelan (W. Ceram); irano (S. Ceram); ai kelane (Ambon); irano (Oeliaser); elan (Boeroe); boes (Marind).

Bark.—Papery, white or grayish.

Wood.—Has reputation of dulling saws quickly, probably because of crystalline inclusions in the cells; should be used in the round and sawing not attempted; generally durable, resistant to teredo and to termites; used for piling in Papua and general building construction in northern Australia.

Occurrence.—Abundant in swamps and dry areas, of the savannah regions and in the swamps of the rain forest of southern Papua; found in Humboldt Bay and probably also occurs further east in Northeast New Guinea.

FIGURE 135.—*Syzygium buettnerianum.*

Syzygium buettnerianum
(Fig. 135)

Habit.—Large tree, spur buttressed.

Leaves.—Opposite, smooth and shining; blade about 4½ by 2½ in.; margins recurved.

Flowers.—The white greenish, pink, red or purple flowers may be borne on the branchlets or on the trunk and main branches.

Fruit.—About ¼ in. to 4 in. long; hard or soft and pithy; contains only one seed.

Bark.—Bright reddish brown, thick, deeply fissured, hard and scaly, fibrous, or peeling in papery flakes.

Wood.—Usually brown or reddish; medium heavy to heavy; medium hard to hard. Wood of several species used for house construction, boatbuilding, railroad ties, etc., in the Philippines.

Occurrence.—From coastal lowlands up to elevations of about 5,000 ft. throughout New Guinea. One of over 100 species known from the region, several of which occur in the Philippines.

Syzygium cumini (Eugenia jambolana) (Fig. 136)

Local Names. Java plum, thabyay-hpyoo (Burma) ; djambeh kelng, djamboe kling, oebor, djamboe kalang (Sumatra) ; djambeland, djamboe djoewat, djiwat (Malayan) ; kjamblang (Sunda Is.) ; doewet, doewet manting, doewet sapi (Java) ; dhalas bato, dhoewak (Madura) ; djoewet, djoedjoe-tan (Bali) ; klajoe (Lombok) ; doeweh (Sumbawa) ; djamboelan (Flores I.).

Habit. Attains 50 to 80 ft. in height and 4 ft. in diameter, with a clear length of 15 to 30 ft.; trunk is often crooked; branchlets are smooth and white.

Leaves. Elliptical to lanceolate, 2 to 4 in. long, with smooth margins, thin, leathery, smooth on both surfaces; petiole about 1 in. long.

Flowers. Small, white, with 4 petals, borne in rigid panicles at old leaf scars and below the younger leafy branchlets.

Fruit. An ovoid, dark purple berry, about 1 in. long with edible pulp, smooth-surfaced and containing a single seed; this species is valued for its fruit throughout the region.

Bark. Gray, about 1 in. thick, fibrous, sheds small rounded flakes.

Wood. Brown, soft but difficult to work, may crack and split if not carefully seasoned; used for house construction in Java; considered resistant to insects.

Occurrence. Usually found below 1,500-ft. elevation, especially in the teak forests; Burma to Formosa and Malay Archipelago. There are several hundred allied species in the region, all with similar wood.

FIGURE 137.—*Tristania suaveolens.*

Tristania suaveolens (Fig. 137)

Local Names.—Swamp mahogany (Australia).

Habit.—Attains 2 ft. in diameter and 100 ft. in height; a slender straight trunk.

Flowers.—White.

Bark.—Reddish-brown, fibrous, fissured.

Wood.—Reddish to dark brown; hard, heavy, brittle, resistant to termites; durable in contact with ground; considered resistant to marine borers and used for salt water piling in Australia.

Occurrence.—Papua; one of principal trees of savannah forests of southern dry belt. Various other species in the genus occur as far north as the Philippine Islands.

FIGURE 138.—*Xanthostemon paradoxus.*

Xanthostemon paradoxus (Fig. 138)

Habit.—Attains 100 ft. in height; trunk cylindrical or slightly fluted or spurred at base.

Leaves.—Leaves are deciduous and tree remains bare for a few days early in September.

Flowers.—Yellow, bloom in profusion just before leaf fall.

Bark.—Dark gray, thick, hard, deeply fissured.

Wood.—Light reddish-brown; rays numerous, reddish, pores small, numerous; parenchyma inconspicuous; grain crossed; texture fine; without distinct taste or odor; very hard and heavy; very strong and durable, but is subject to checking in drying; growth rings not prominent; a good hard wood.

Occurrence.—Papua; common to abundant in dry area savannah forest on ridges, especially near edge of rain forest and within drier edge of rain forest.

Xanthostemon verdugonianus (Fig. 139)

Local Names.—Buongan, malapiga (Culion); bungan (Palawan); tiga (Sibuyan); tamulauan (Leyte); magkono (Surigao, Tinago, Dinagat, Leyte, Agusan). The wood is sometimes referred to as "Philippine lignum vitae," "Philippine iron wood," or "palo de hierro."

Habit.—A small to medium sized tree attaining 60 in. in diameter with 30 ft. of main stem; trunk is generally short but regular, and the branches usually extend down 3 to 6 ft. from the ground.

Leaves.—1½ to 3 in. by 2½ to 4 in., smooth, whitish beneath.

Flowers.—Borne in terminal cymes, purple.

Fruit.—A small dry capsule; opens by 2 to 3 valves, has many minute seeds.

Bark.—Thin, smooth, very hard.

Wood.—Sapwood ½ to 1 in. thick, light brown, not sharply demarcated from reddish-brown heartwood; heartwood turns very dark brown with age; rays very narrow, numerous, lighter in color than the surrounding tissue; pores nearly all isolated, diffuse, small, moderately numerous, filled with tyloses and with dark red gummy deposits, or with softer yellow deposits; parenchyma inconspicuous; specific gravity, air-dry, 1.411; grain nearly always crossed, texture fine, glossy, without distinct odor or taste; very heavy, considered the heaviest of the Philippine woods; very hard and strong; ends of logs subject to severe checking and should be painted with heavy oil to retard end drying; very difficult to work, very durable, even under most severe conditions; the most durable of the Philippines woods; suitable for posts, poles, salt water piling, tool

362

handles, paper weights, pulleys, rollers, bearings, steering bushings, or ship propellers and other uses for which an extremely hard, heavy, durable wood is required.

Occurrence.—Philippines; Sibuyan, Busuanga Cuilon, Palawan, Samar, Leyte, Panay, Tinago, Dinagat, and Mindanao; local occurrence is scattered to numerous; a fair quantity may be obtained; other species of this genus present in New Guinea.

FIGURE 139.—*Xanthostemon verdugonianus*

Sapotaceae

(Sapote or Chicle Family)

Trees and shrubs sometimes armed with spines; sap always milky; leaves simple and alternate, with smooth margins; fruit pulpy; inner bark, pith and leaves have tubes which secrete fats, gums, and latex-like substances. Some species (*Palaquium spp.*) produce gutta percha, and others (*Achras spp.*) produce chicle.

Madhuca betis (see Fig. 140 for similar species)

Local Names.—Pianga, piangan, ubien, malini (Cagayan); bakayao (La Union, Pangasinan); gatasan (Pangasinan); betis (Zambales, Papangas, Tayabas, Camarines, Cavite); gattatar (Nueva Ecija); baetis (Bataan); batis (Rizal); malaputat (Tayabas); baniti, banite na pula, banitis (Camarines).

Habit.—A large tree attaining 50 in. in diameter, and 25 to 35 ft. of main stem; trunk generally straight, with large buttresses.

Leaves.—Simple, large, pubescent, borne at tips of the branchlets.

Flowers.—Pale green, borne in clusters on the branchlets.

Fruit.—Ovoid, fleshy, containing a single large, hard shiny seed.

Bark.—Yellowish.

Wood.—Sapwood 4 to 8 in. thick, light, distinctly demarcated from the light brown heartwood; rays narrow, numerous; pores in groups, diffuse, tyloses present; parenchyma diffuse, consisting of numerous short, narrow, tangential lines extending between the rays; specific gravity, air-dry, 0.827; texture fine, glossy, grain straight or slightly crossed; taste bitter, without distinct odor; it lathers freely when rubbed with water; hard and strong, seasons well with very little defect, is hard to saw but not difficult to finish; very durable, even when exposed or in contact with the ground; resistant to marine borers; suitable for wharf, bridge and ship construction, posts, foundations, ties, paving blocks, and for tool handles; suitable for any purpose requiring strength and durability.

Occurrence.—Confined to the island of Luzon (Philippines), found at low altitudes; supply is very limited.

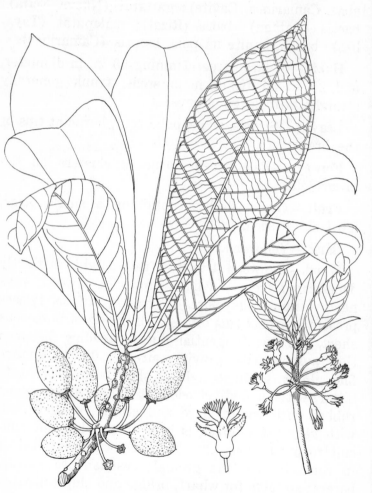

FIGURE 140.—*Bassia betis*

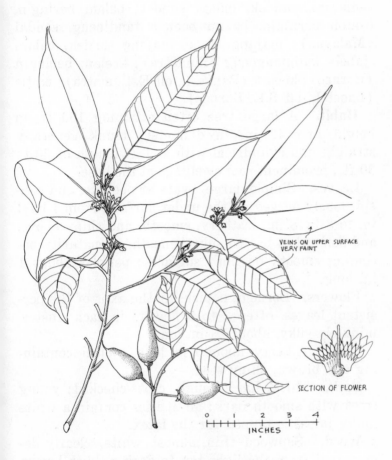

VEINS ON UPPER SURFACE
VERY FAINT

SECTION OF FLOWER

0 1 2 3 4
INCHES

FIGURE 141. *Madhuca leerii*

367

Madhuca leerii (Payena leerii) (Fig. 141)

Local Names. Balam sundik (Sumatra) ; sunian, semaram, sundek, balam sundek, balam beringin, njatoh beringin, balam boenga tandjoeng, sondai (Malayan) ; majang batoe, majang sondek, balam tjabeh, kalimangoeng (Sumatra) ; koelan, beringin (Borneo) ; koelan (Banka I., off E. Sumatra) ; baitis (Laoet I., off S.E. Borneo).

Habit. A large tree often attaining 100 ft. in height and 40 in. in diameter; trunk generally straight and cylindrical with a clear length of 20 to 30 ft.; prominent root swellings at the base.

Leaves. Simple, large, ovate or obovate, and conspicuously nerved on the under surface, from 1 by 4 in. to 3 by 8 in., leathery, smooth, and shiny above, and somewhat brown-silky beneath, at maturity becoming smooth on both surfaces; petioles about 1 in. long.

Flowers. Borne in panicles in the axils of the persistent leaves, often 2 to 6 flowers in each cluster, minutely silky, about ½ in. long.

Fruit. A berry, about 1 in. long, conical, containing one brown, shiny seed.

Bark. Thick, hard, rough, cross-checked; young trees with smooth bark; all species contain a white milky juice; is tapped for the latex.

Wood. Sapwood thin, almost white, clearly demarcated from the light tan to dark reddish-brown heartwood; grain straight, texture fine; dull in appearance, may have a bitter taste; moderately heavy, hard, and strong; growth rings generally indistinct, marked by terminal parenchyma; pores generally in groups, small, few in number; parenchyma diffuse or in narrow concentric bands; rays very narrow, numerous; very durable even when exposed or in contact with the ground, resistant to attack of marine borers; suitable for wharf, bridge, and ship building, posts, railroad ties, paving blocks, and for all general uses requiring strength and durability.

Occurrence. Widely distributed, Burma to Indo-China, southward to Java, Borneo, Malay Archipelago.

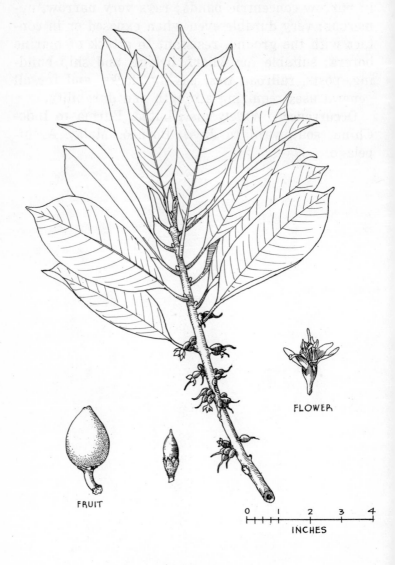

FLOWER

FRUIT

0 1 2 3 4
INCHES

FIGURE 142. *Palaquium gutta*

Palaquium gutta (Fig. 142)

Local Names. Gutta-percha, getah percha, taban merah, nyatoh barak, balam abang, balem merah, taban merah, getah taban, ekor daun durian (Malay Peninsula) ; majang doerian, majang merah, doerian taban, balam doerian (Sumatra) ; njatoh doerian, njatoh temiang samboen (Borneo).

Habit. Attains 100 ft. in height.

Leaves. Leathery, dark green above, golden coppery below, obovate to oblanceolate, with prominent midrib, 1½ by 3 in. to 2½ by 5 in.

Flowers. Borne in axillary fascicles of 4 or 5, white, petals ¼ in. long.

Fruit. A berry, ½ to 1 in. long, red, with fine hairs, containing one or two seeds.

Bark. Tapped for gutta percha.

Wood. Sapwood is narrow, light in color, not sharply demarcated from the red heartwood; grain generally straight but may be wavy or curly; texture fine; glossy; without distinct taste or odor; light to heavy, fairly strong; considered fairly durable for interior use but not durable when exposed or in contact with the ground; growth rings indistinct, marked by dense wood within the growth rings; pores generally in groups, small, few in number; parenchyma in concentric lines and diffuse; rays narrow, numerous; easy to work, suitable for cabinetmaking, patternmaking, and boat decking.

Occurrence. Malay Peninsula, Borneo; many allied species throughout the region.

Palaquim luzoniense (Fig. 143)

Local Names.—Araka (Cagayan); niket (Ilocos Norte); gasatanga na lipaoen, gatasan (Ilocos Sur); takaran (Pangasinan); pateleo (Nueva Ecija); tagatoi, palak-palak (Bataan); nato (Bataan, Tayabas, Laguna, Mindoro); dolitan or dulitan, gatasan (Tayabas); tinykayad (Rizal).

Habit.—A large tree to 60 in. in diameter with 30 to 35 ft. of main stem, straight without buttresses.

Leaves.—Simple, alternate, smooth, 2 to 3 in. x 4 to 8 in.

Flowers.—Parts of the flowers are in sixes; borne in axils of the leaves of the branchlets.

Fruit.—A berry, small, ovid, with one or two hard shiny seeds.

Bark.—½ to 1 in. thick, gray to brown, has vertical fissures; inner bark is granular, red in color, brittle and exudes a milky juice when cut.

Wood.—Sapwood 1 to 2 in. thick, not sharply demarcated from the reddish-brown heartwood, growth rings indistinct; rays narrow, numerous; pores small, few in number, in groups; parenchyma in short tangential lines and in wavy continuous lines; specific gravity, air-dry, 0.475 to 0.882, average 0.678; straight grained, occasionally wavy, fine texture, glossy, without definite taste or odor, seasons well, easy to work, moderately durable for interior work, but not durable when exposed or in contact with the ground. Because of freedom from warping it is widely used for the sides and bottoms of drawers and shelves in wardrobes and other furniture. It also makes good patterns and has been used for ship planking.

Occurrence.—Philippines; Luzon, Mindoro, Sibuyan, Masbate, and Guimara; common in virgin forests at medium and low altitudes; the total supply is small. Many other species in this genus are present in the region, Philippines to New Guinea.

FIGURE 143.- *Palaquim luzoniense*

FIGURE 144.—*Planchonella paludosa*

Planchonella paludosa (Fig. 144)

Habit.—A large tree, to 36 in. in diameter and 100 ft. in height, often with 50 ft. of clear length; trunk straight and cylindrical, without buttresses.

Leaves.—Simple, entire, ovate, 2 to 4 in., long, dark green, glossy above and pubescent below, with numerous conspicuous veins.

Flowers.—Small, yellowish - green, crowded in small clumps on the twigs.

Fruit.—A large berry.

Bark.—About 1 in. thick, light to dark gray, sometimes slightly brownish; with hard, brittle, plate-like scales.

Wood.—Sapwood thin and creamy white, heartwood pinkish-brown; rays fine, numerous, sinuous about the pores, clearly visible, not conspicuous on radial surface; pores small, slightly flattened tangentially, arranged in radial rows between the rays; parenchyma abundant, arranged in inconspicuous irregular concentric lines; moderately hard, heavy and strong, straight-grained, works readily, blue-stains unless properly seasoned soon after felling, is not considered durable; suitable for general temporary construction and for making handles and other small articles.

Occurrence.—New Guinea and Philippines; other species of this genus widely distributed through the region.

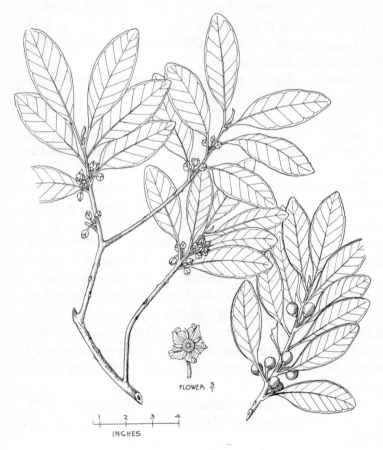

FLOWER $\frac{3}{1}$

FIGURE 145. *Sideroxylon ferrugineum*

Sideroxylon ferrugineum (Fig. 145)

Local Names. Barat laut, nasi-nasi merah, tawak, tuak-tuak, binasi, njatch (Malayan); balam timah (West central Sumatra); djengkok, pantjal, tjeng-kek (Java); arnana (Flores I.).

Habit. Attains a diameter of 30 in. with a clear length of about 30 ft., trunk is straight and regular; branchlets rust-colored.

Leaves. Simple, elliptical, smooth, on both surfaces, 1¼ by 3 in., leathery; petiole ½ in. long.

Flowers. Borne in axillary panicles.

Fruit. A smooth, shiny berry, about ½ in. in diameter and with 1 to 2 hard, shiny seeds.

Wood. Sapwood not distinct from the light yellow heartwood; growth rings indistinct; pores nearly all in groups of 2 to 8, very small, numerous, without tyloses; parenchyma in concentric lines and terminal at the ends of growth rings, conspicuous, wavy, narrow, numerous; rays narrow, indistinct, numerous; straight-grained, fine-textured, glossy in appearance, without characteristic taste or odor; very heavy, hard, and strong; specific gravity, air-dry, 1.114; ends of logs are liable to split and check; easy to work; rated as durable; used for house posts, salt-water piling, and small articles such as tool handles.

Occurrence. Usually along the beaches but is not abundant; Andamans, Malay Peninsula, Borneo, Southern China; many similar allied species present in the region.

377

Ebenaceae

(Ebony Family)

Trees and shrubs widely distributed in tropical and sub-tropical parts of the world; leaves alternate, dark-green, and leathery; woods hard, heavy, and durable; heartwood usually black and bark astringent; fruit of a few species edible.

FLOWER

0 1 2 3 4
INCHES

FIGURE 147. *Maba buxifolia*

FIGURE 146. *Diospyros pilosanthera*

379

Diospyros pilosanthera (Fig. 146)

Local Names.—Philippines: Bantulinoi, mabulo ti bakes, mago-ilum, puagan (Babuyanes); balingagta (Cagayan, Isabela, Ilocos Norte, Ilocos Sur, Pangasinan, Nueva Ecija); balatinao (Ilocos Norte); ditman (Isabela); galarigar (Pangasinan); malatalang (Tarlac, Pampagna); bolong-eta, bulong-eta (Cagayan, Nueva Ecija, Tayabas, Zambales, Bataan, Laguna, Batangas, Mindoro, Zamboanga); malagaitman, malapuyao (Tayabas); kulantiaga, pugat (Nueva Ecija); atilma, dambuhala, katilma (Rizal); talang-gubat (Laguna); bagonito, nito-nito (Camarines Norte, Sorsogon, Samar); anam, ata-ata, marakibal (Camarines Sur); tanne (Samar); nita-ata (Iloilo); tagsai (Cebu), tamil, tamil-babae (Lanao, Davao); palo-negro, magalitum (Davao); belat-belat (Sulu). New Guinea: bana (Suku), gah-a (Buna), ka-uka (Vailala).

Habit.—Attains 40 in. in diameter and with 15 to 30 ft. of main stem; the trunk is regular and without buttresses.

Leaves.—Alternate, simple, smooth or with few scattered white hairs beneath, 2 to 4 in. x 4 to 8 in.

Flowers.—White, bell-shaped, borne singly or in clusters at bases of the leaves; male and female flowers on separate trees.

Fruit.—Yellow or red, hard, fleshy, ½ to ¾ in. in diameter; contains several hard black seeds.

Bark.—Greenish-black, ¼ in. thick, with jagged, short, spiny projections; inner bark light red.

Wood.—Sapwood is thick, reddish; heartwood is relatively small in diameter, black with streaks of red; growth rings are indistinct; rays very narrow, indistinct, very numerous, lighter than surrounding tissue; pores mostly in groups, diffuse, small; par-

380

enchyma in wavy, narrow, concentric lines, extending between the rays; specific gravity, air-dry, 0.902 to 0.967, average 0.935; grain is straight, texture fine; glossy, without distinct taste or odor, very heavy, hard and strong, difficult to season as it is liable to split and warp; tough, difficult to work; durable, even when exposed or in contact with the ground; has been used for all the purposes for which ebony is employed.

Occurrence.—Philippines from Babuyanes and northern Luzon to Palawan and Mindanao; common at low altitudes. In the past only the larger trees with fairly large heartwood have been cut for timber; small quantities are generally obtainable. Many other species in the genus occur throughout the region to New Guinea.

Maba buxifolia (Fig. 147)

Local Names. Ebony; kaya arang, kayu arang, secherek laut, riboe-riboe, sachinit laut (Malay Peninsula); poeloet (Banka I., off E. Sumatra); rangkemi (S.E. Sumatra, Lampong); ki merak (Sunda Is.); bibis, keloran, merakan (Java).

Habit. A small tree.

Leaves. Elliptical or obovate, leathery, blade ¼ by ¼ in. to ½ by 1 in.; petiole ½ in. long.

Flowers. Solitary or 2 to 3 borne in a cyme.

Fruit. Globose, ½ in. long, bearing one seed.

Wood. Sapwood thick, pinkish, clearly demarcated from the black heartwood; heartwood may contain reddish longitudinal stripes; grain straight or slightly crossed; texture fine; without characteristic taste or odor; very hard and heavy; sapwood tough, heartwood brittle; difficult to season, warps and shrinks easily if not properly seasoned; growth rings indistinct; pores isolated and in groups, very small, few to numerous, contain black deposits; parenchyma in concentric bands, conspicuous, wavy, narrow, numerous; rays very narrow and numerous; suitable for temporary construction, durable for interior work but not durable when exposed or in contact with the ground.

Occurrence. Near the coast; Malay Peninsula, and generally throughout the region.

Loganaceae

(Logania Family)

Trees, shrubs, or herbs; leaves opposite, smooth-margined or toothed; flowers small to large, variously arranged; fruit capsular, or drupaceous. The species inhabit chiefly the tropical countries and are bitter and highly poisonous. *Strychnos nuxvomica* the source of strychnine, belongs to this family.

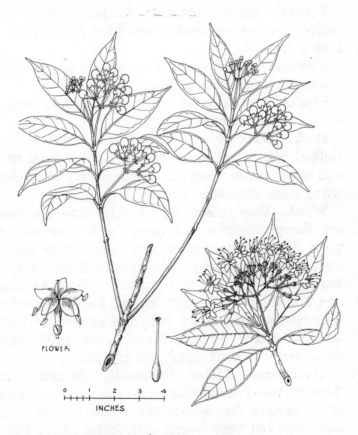

FLOWER

INCHES

FIGURE 148. *Fagraea fragrans*

Fagraea fragrans (Fig. 148)

Local Names. Tembusu, tembusu luar, lemesu, meriang, reriang, temesu, tembesoe paja, tembesoe rawang, tembesoe renah (Malayan).

Habit. A medium-sized tree, attains about 20 in. in diameter and 100 ft. in height, has a large crown, rather open, and with a fairly short, clear length; trunk is somewhat irregular and with small buttresses.

Leaves. Simple, opposite, leathery, shiny, with entire margins, somewhat wrinkled, ¾ by 3 in. to 1 by 5 in.

Flowers. Borne in axillary or terminal panicles, waxy, cream-colored, and quite fragrant.

Fruit. A globose berry, scarlet or orange-red, ¼ to ½ in. in diameter.

Bark. Dark grayish-brown, with narrow, longitudinal ridges and deep fissures; outer bark corky and dark yellow when cut; inner bark yellow, darkening upon exposure; 0.4 to 0.5 in. thick.

Wood. Pale yellow with pinkish tinge; sapwood not sharply demarcated from the heartwood; sapwood darkens upon exposure; ranges from hard to very hard, very heavy and strong; without taste but has a distinctly acid odor; is very difficult to season and difficult to work; durable and has been used for construction in contact with the ground or water, and for heavy timbers, house posts, shipbuilding, furniture, cabinetmaking, and carving.

Occurrence. Malay Peninsula, Sumatra, and Borneo; wood of similar quality is produced by related species throughout the western tropics; not abundant but very widely distributed; from 100- to 800-ft. elevation; often found as planted trees.

Apocynaceae

Trees and upright or climbing shrubs, rarely herbs, distributed mostly throughout the tropical countries; many species yield poisonous, acrid and milky secretions, while others yield elastic gum and edible fruits; a number have been introduced as horticultural subjects.

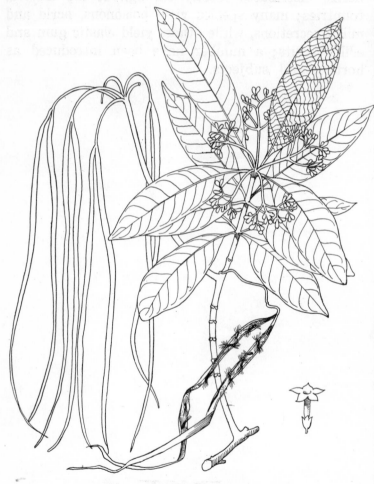

FIGURE 149.—*Alstonia macrophylla*

Alstonia macrophylla (Fig. **149**)

Local Names. Beburus, buta-buta darat, changgai puteri, medang tahi kerbau (Malay Peninsula); melaboewai (Palembang, S.E. Sumatra). Philippines: buisisi, pangolaksien (Cagayan); basikal, basikarang, batikalag, batikalang (Cagayan, Ilocos Sur, Isabela, Pangasinan); manggamanga, maramangga (Cagayan, La Union); banakao, pangalanutien, pangalunadsin (Ilocos Norte); dalakan, darakan (Ilocos Sur); kalatuche, pangalisokloen (Pangasinan); batino (Rizal, Laguna, Cavite, Batangas, Tayabas, Camarines, Mindoro); itang-itang (Tayabas, Guimares); buyaoyao, kuyao-kuyao (Camarines Sur, Catanduanes, Capiz); dita-dita (Albay); pugayan, tugayan (Mindoro); malabato (Marinduque); lasona (Samar); oponopong (Leyte); tangitang, ughagan (Capiz); dinog (Bohol); kurayan, rigayan, sulusilhigan (Palawan); guala (Bukidnon); tulingan (Sibutu); sakian, tamballongon (Sulu).

Habit. Attains 32 in. in diameter and 70 ft. in height, with 30 ft. of clear length; trunk is straight and regular, without buttresses.

Leaves. Simple, obovate, opposite or in whorles, smooth margins, 2 by 6 in. to 3 by 12 in.; petiole ¼ in. long.

Flowers. Small, white, fragrant, numerous; borne in terminal cymes or whorled panicles.

Fruit. Two slender cylindrical pods, to 1 ft. long.

Bark. Gray, ½ in. thick, smooth, with pustules in irregular longitudinal lines; inner bark yellow; exudes latex.

Wood. Sapwood not sharply demarcated from the pale yellow-brown heartwood; rays narrow, numerous; pores in groups of 2 to 14, diffuse, small, numerous; parenchyma diffuse, consisting of small dots between the rays; growth rings absent; specific gravity, air-dry, 0.760; grain crossed, often wavy; texture fine; taste bitter, but without odor; heavy, hard and strong; may warp and check during seasoning; easy to work and takes a high finish; durable when exposed or in contact with the ground; has been used for general construction, flooring, and household implements; because of attractive grain, it is suitable for high grade furniture and cabinet making.

Occurrence. Throughout the region; common in the open virgin forests and in secondary forests, at low and medium altitudes; obtainable only in small quantities; other species in the genus present in the region.

FIGURE 150.—*Alstonia scholaris.*

Alstonia scholaris (Fig. 150)

Local Names. Basong, pulai basong, rejang, kajoe gaboes, kajoe, skola, poelai (Malayan); handjaloetoeng (Dayak country, S. Borneo); lameh(Sunda Is.); poeleh (Java); polaj (Madura); kaliti, reareangow, bariangow (N. Celebes); rita (Makassar, Ambon); lita-lita (Boegina); aliag (W. New Guinea); leleko, rangere, angere (N. Halmahera); hange (Ternate). New Guinea: didma (Buna); sawa (New Britain); devoru (Motu); aijapo (Vailala); amika (Evara, Delta Division).

Habit. Attains 3 ft. in diameter and 120 ft. in height, with 90 ft. of clear length; spreading branches; trunk narrowly flanged or fluted.

Leaves. Simple, whorled, lanceolate, leathery, dark green above and light green below, exude latex when broken; blade 2 by 4 in., petiole ½ in. long.

Flowers. White, borne in panicles.

Fruit. Paired, long, slender, pendulous pods.

Bark. Pale gray, 1 in. thick, slightly scaly; inner bark yellow; exudes abundant milky latex when cut.

Wood. Sapwood pale yellow; heartwood not differentiated by color; rays fine, straight, dark yellow; parenchyma in wavy lines; specific gravity, 0.514; soft and light; suitable for inside work; has been used for butter boxes; requires careful seasoning to avoid blue-staining.

Occurrence. Throughout the region; common on river flats and mountain slopes up to 2,000 ft.; occurs in both the luxuriant rain forest and the drier "monsoon" forest; Burma to Indo-China, Hainan and Formosa, and throughout the Malay Archipelago; this is one of several species of this genus present in the region.

Verbenaceae

(Vervain or Teak Family)

Trees and shrubs, widely distributed throughout the tropical world principally in the southern hemisphere. The most important generic groups are *Tectona* (teak), *Vitex* (molave of the Philippines) and *Avicennia* (white mangrove) ; all large trees furnish important timbers; leaves usually opposite and entire; bark of some species used for tanning; leaves, bark, and fruit of different species used medicinally by the natives of India and elsewhere.

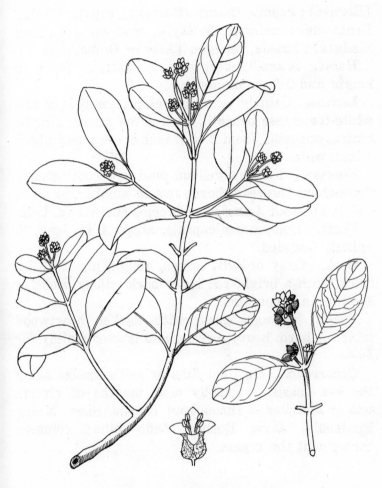

FIGURE 151. *Avicennia marina*

Avicennia marina (Fig. 151)

Local Names. White mangrove; Appi appi (Borneo); caemb, thame (Burma); cepate (Malay Peninsula); api-api (Malayan, and on Java and Madura); kausia, renggou (Alor or Ombay I.).

Habit. A small, evergreen tree; attains 80 ft. in height and 2 ft. in diameter.

Leaves. Usually lanceolate-elliptic or oblong and white-tomentose beneath, dark-green above; simple, entire, opposite, from 2 to 3 inches long, and about 1 inch wide.

Flowers. Flowers yellow, produced continuously throughout the year; borne few in number, in short spikes on stout 4-angled peduncles about 1 in. long.

Fruit. Compressed capsule, about 1 in. long, 2-valved, 1-seeded.

Bark, Gray or light brown, rough, about ½ in. thick, with a bright-red inner bark widely used for the tannin it contains.

Wood. Sapwood gray, with darker heartwood which is hard, heavy, brittle, and is used mainly for fuel.

Occurrence. On tidal flats or salt marshes along the sea coasts, especially near mouths of rivers; widely distributed throughout Burma, Siam, Malay Peninsula, Java, Borneo, Indo-China; common throughout the region.

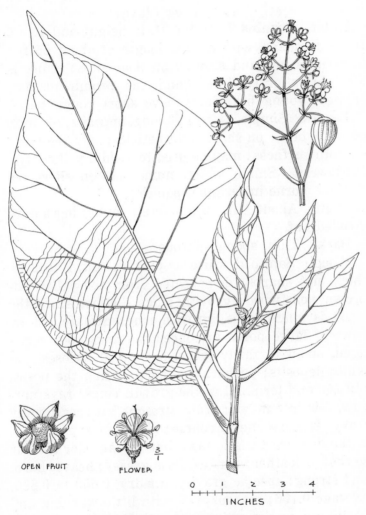

OPEN FRUIT

FLOWER

$\frac{3}{1}$

0 1 2 3 4

INCHES

FIGURE 152. *Tectona grandis*

393

Tectona grandis (Fig. 152)

Local Names. Teak, kyoon-pen (Burma); teak, jati (Malay Peninsula); teck, teak, dodolan (Sunda Islands); djati, djatos, deleg (Java).

Habit. Attains 70 to 100 ft. in height and 4 to 5 ft. in diameter, with a clear length of about 65 ft.; sometimes low and stunted on poor sites; trunk is straight, slightly fluted, and has prominent buttresses; young branchlets have short rough hairs.

Leaves. Simple, ½ to 1 ft. long, opposite, ovate to obovate, borne on short stout petioles; soft fine hairs on both surfaces; may be used to yield a yellow dye.

Flowers. Small, white, numerous, on short peduncles, borne in terminal panicles.

Fruit. About 1 in. in diameter, containing a hard 4-celled nut.

Bark. Thin, spongy-fibrous.

Wood. Sapwood white or pinkish-buff, 1 to 2 in. thick, not sharply demarcated from the yellowish-brown heartwood; growth rings distinct since the wood is ring-porous; growth rings demarcated by rows of large pores in concentric rings; pores isolated, small to fairly large, some with tyloses and white deposits; parenchyma surrounding the pores, diffuse, and terminal in the growth rings; rays narrow, few in number; grain straight but occasionally wavy; texture fine to coarse; glossy in appearance; without characteristic taste but has an odor similar to that of leather; surface feels greasy; heavy, hard, and strong; specific gravity, air-dry, 0.650 to 0.885, average 0.796; seasons well with little warping and shrinking, works easily, takes a high polish; durable in interior work, and when exposed to the weather and in contact with the ground; is considered moderately resistant to marine borers and noted for its dimensional stability under changes in surrounding conditions; has been used for shipbuilding, furniture, interior finish, plywood, and for all purposes requiring durability and strength; its oil is used as a substitute for linseed oil in paint.

Occurrence. Up to 3,000 ft.; Burma and Siam, and is extensively planted in Java.

FIGURE 153.—*Vitex cofassus.*

Vitex cofassus (Fig. 153)

Local Names.—New Guinea teak, anoano (Doura), tato-o (Buna), bai-ah (Vailala), ka-ar (Yabim), afas (Yalu); ahsang (Rabaul); boepasa, gofasa (Malayan, Moluccas); katondeng (Makassar); biti, katonde (Boegina); pasal (S. Ceram); banafat, banohoeba (Soela I.); beso (S. Halmahera); gawasa (N. Halmahera).

Habit.—A medium-sized tree, to 2½ ft. in diameter and 70 ft. in height; with a grooved, gnarled trunk.

Leaves.—Simple, opposite, in pairs alternately crossing at right angles; petiole ¾ to 2 in. long; blade 4 to 7 in. by ¼ to 3 in., lanceolate, glabrous, thin; stem square in cross-sections.

Fruit.—A drupe, small, somewhat fleshy, with 2 to 4 seeds, acrid and aromatic.

Bark.—About ¼ in. thick, pale brown, papery, smooth; inner bark white streaked with yellow.

Wood.—Sapwood yellow, 3 in. thick; heartwood deep brown; rays 100 per in., pale yellow, slightly sinuous around pores, very fine; pores 5,500 to 7,000 per sq. in., in zones, very minute; parenchyma in thin lines, about 10 per in.; straight grain; satiny figure on radial surface; cuts hard; specific gravity about 0.705; used for canoe paddles; can be used as general utility wood; considered durable in contact with ground in New Ireland but not on New Guinea.

Occurrence.—Common or scattered on well-drained lowlands or lower mountain slopes; New Guinea, Bismarcks and Solomons; this is one of several tree species in this genus in this region.

FRUIT

0 1 2 3 4
INCHES

FLOWER 2/1

2⅓/1

FIGURE 154. *Vitex glabrata*

Vitex glabrata (Fig. 154)

Local Names. Bihboel (Sunda Islands); tileng, gentileng, ketileng, laban ketilang (Java); boetboet (Kangeang I., off N.E. Java).

Habit. Attains 35 in. in diameter and 75 ft. in height.

Leaves. Digitately compound, with 5 leaflets.

Flowers. Irregular, small, blue, borne in many-flowered panicles.

Fruit. A drupe, ½ in. long.

Bark. Smooth, white.

Wood. Sapwood light, not distinct from the light yellow heartwood; growth rings distinct but irregular, marked by occurrence of pores; pores isolated and in groups of 2 to 4, small, numerous; parenchyma indistinct; rays narrow, few in number; grain straight or somewhat wavy; texture fine; dull in appearance; without characteristic taste or odor; heavy, hard, and strong; seasons with very little checking or splitting; works easily; durable in interior work; moderately durable when exposed and in contact with the ground; has been used for general house construction and furniture making.

Occurrence. Common, often in association with teak *(Tectona grandis)*; makes its best development on well-drained sites; Andamans, Burma, to Indo-China and Malaysia; many similar allied species present in the region.

FIGURE 155. *Vitex parviflora*

Vitex parviflora (V. altissima) (Fig. 155)

Local Names. Kajoe koela (Malayan).

Habit. Attains 100 in. in diameter but the trunk is short, crooked, fluted, and with large buttresses; crown is dense and branchlets are 4-sided.

Leaves. Digitately compound, with 3 or rarely 5 leaflets.

Flowers. Irregular, blue, small, borne in many-flowered panicles.

Fruit. A small, purple drupe.

Bark. Gray, scaly; inner bark yellow and fibrous.

Wood. Sapwood narrow, light-colored, not distinct from the yellowish-brown heartwood; growth rings distinct, marked by dark and light wood and fine terminal parenchyma; pores nearly all isolated, small, numerous, nearly all with tyloses; parenchyma inconspicuous, terminal parenchyma in fine, continuous lines; rays narrow, numerous; grain crossed, inclined to be wavy; texture fine; glossy in appearance; without distinct taste or odor; heavy, hard, and brittle; specific gravity, air-dry, 0.938; seasons well with little shrinking, easy to work, takes a high polish; durable under all conditions except when exposed to marine borers; used for high-grade construction, shipbuilding, posts, railroad ties, paving blocks, carving, furniture, flooring, windows and doors, and wherever strength and durability are required.

Occurrence. Borneo; similar and allied species present in the region.

Rubiaceae
(Madder Family)

Trees and shrubs, often herbs, distributed in many parts of both temperate and tropical regions; includes the coffee and cinchona trees. The numerous members of this family are characterized by the presence of many alkaloids and glucosides together with some essential oils, fats, dyes, and valuable drugs. The leaves are opposite or whorled.

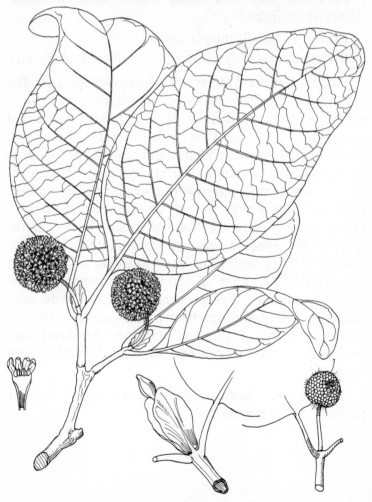

FIGURE 157.—*Nauclea undulata*

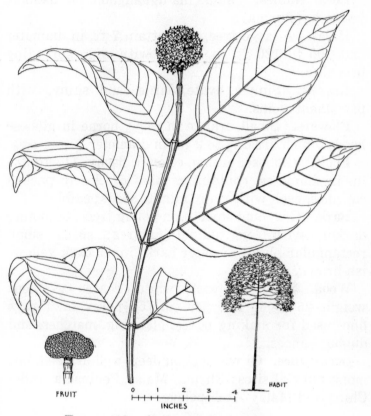

FRUIT   HABIT

FIGURE 156. *Anthocephalus cadamba*

403

Anthocephalus cadamba (Fig. 156)

Local Names. Ma-u, ma-uguangdôn, ma-ukadôn, ye-ma-u (Burma).

Habit. A large tree, may attain 7 ft. in diameter and 100 to 120 ft. in height, with wide spreading branches.

Leaves. Simple, ovate, large, and shiny, with prominent veins.

Flowers. Small, orange in color, borne in globose heads which are 1½ to 2 in. in diameter.

Fruit. Globose, orange-colored, fleshy, 1½ to 2½ in. in diameter, containing mass of closely packed capsules, each with many minute seeds; edible.

Bark. Gray and smooth on young trees, becoming darker, with longitudinal fissures; sheds small rectangular plates of outer bark; inner bark yellowish-brown.

Wood. Soft, yellowish - white, coarse - grained; weight 25 to 50 lbs. per cu. ft.; pores few; rays fine; used for making boxes, planking, matches, and dugout canoes.

Occurrence. Grows best on deep, well-drained, but moist alluvial sites; Burma, Malay Peninsula, Indo-China and Malay Archipelago.

Nauclea orientalis (*Sarcocephalus cordatus*)
(see Fig.157 for similar species)

Local Names.—Gempol (Malayan) ; kajoe mas (Minahassa) ; menin (S. Halmahera) ; New Guinea : seha, tiga, ziga (Buna) ; ziga (Binendele) ; aruntimf (Lower Markham Valley) ; sabi (Suku) ; peopoia (Vailala). Philippines : Bulala (Camiguin, Cagayan, Mountain Province, Ilocos Norte, Ilocos Sur, La Union, Pangasinan) ; bangkal (Pangasinan, Zambales, Tarlac, Pampanga, Rizal, Bataan, Manila, Laguna, Cavite, Tayabas, Batangas, Mindoro) ; bankal (Leyte, Negros Occidental, Ticao, Cotabato, Palawan) ; mambog, manbog (Tayabas, Camarines, Albay) ; bankao (Leyte) ; bakal (Capiz) ; bolobituan (Negros Occidental) ; kabag, kabak, malbog (Samar, Agusan) ; gimbalud (Bukidnon) ; balikakae (Cotabato) ; makabak (Davao) ; barikarob (Zamboanga).

Habit.—Attains 3 ft. in diameter and 90 ft. in height with 60 ft. of clear length ; without buttresses ; branches whorled.

Leaves.—Simple, opposite, yellowish-green ; petiole 1¾ in. long, twisted ; blade 8 to 15 in. by 5 to 9 in., ovate, smooth above, with soft hairs below.

Bark.—Light brown, corky, scaly, often twisting spirally around the bole ; inner bark yellow, corky, with bitter taste.

Wood.—White to pale yellow, or white to dark yellow, sapwood not demarcated from heartwood.

> **White Wood Type.**—Rays 180 to 200 per in., yellow, slightly sinuous, not prominent on radial surface ; pores conspicuous, 2,400 to 2,500 per sq. in., fairly evenly scattered, few concentric narrow bands, fine grain ; specific gravity 0.529, cuts soft and clean.

Yellow Wood Type.—Rays 250 per in., yellow, appear as dark rectangles on radial surface, sinuous around pores; pores conspicuous, 4,000 to 5,000 per sq. in., evenly scattered; specific gravity 0.625; cuts soft and clean; good for light construction purposes.

Texture is fine, grain slightly crossed, dull appearance, feels greasy; fairly hard and strong, seasons well with little checking but has a tendency to warp; works and finishes well, is satisfactory for interior work, and durable when exposed or in contact with the ground. It has been used for furniture and cabinet work and general house construction.

Occurrence.—Throughout the region; found on most of the islands of the Philippines from Batanes and northern Luzon to Palawan and Mindanao; occurs mainly in the second growth forests at low and medium altitudes on moist sites.

GLOSSARY OF BOTANICAL AND TECHNICAL TERMS

Acrid. Sharp and harsh or bitter and hot.

Acuminate. Sharply pointed; with a long slender sharp point.

Alkali. Soda ash; several substances such as soda, potash and ammonia characterized by their peculiar taste and their forming salts with acids; the stronger ones are caustic.

Alkaloid. An organic substance occurring naturally in plants and with alkaline or basic properties.

Alluvial flat. The delta-like deposit formed by a stream where it issues out upon an open plain.

Alternate pinnate leaflets. Leaflets borne alternately along the sides of the stalk.

Aromatic. Fragrant; strong scented.

Astringent. Drawing together the tissues, binding, contracting.

Axial Panicle. Borne at the intersections of the twig with some other plant organ such as a leaf.

Axil. Angle formed by a branch with a stem of a leaf.

Axillary. Borne at the intersection of a leaf stem with a twig or branch.

Banyan. A tropical tree which starts life supported by a host tree and later extends its roots to the ground, strangling the host. It is of no value for timber production.

Bole. Trunk, stem of tree.

Brackish swamp. Salt water swamp.

Bract. A leaf from the axil of which a flower arises or a leaf borne on the floral axis itself.

Buttress. Horizontally projected portions of the base of the trunk.

Calyx. Collection of sepals which encloses the rest of the flower parts in the bud.

Canopy. The top layer of forest growth formed by the intermingled branches and foliage of adjacent trees.

Checking.	Formation of small cracks or splits in the wood.
Chicle.	The gummy sap of the sapodilla tree used as the basis for chewing gum.
Compound leaf.	A leaf made up of two or more leaflets.
Concentric.	With a common center; parallel.
Conifers.	Trees which bear fruit in the form of a woody cone with scales.
Coriaceous.	Leathery.
Corrugated.	Wrinkled or furrowed; alternate ridges and grooves.
Deciduous.	Leaves fall periodically.
Dehiscence.	The bursting open of a capsule or pod at maturity.
Demarcated.	Separated or bounded.
Disseminate.	Distribute.
Drupe.	A one-seeded fleshy fruit with a hard "stone" or "pit".
Entire.	With smooth margins; without indentations.
Ellipsoid.	A solid body, elliptical in outline.
Epiphyte.	A plant which grows upon another living plant.
Equilibrium moisture content.	The moisture content of air-dry woods at the temperature and humidity of the surrounding air.
Exserted.	Thrust out; protruding; projecting beyond some enclosing organ or part.
Exude.	Ooze out.
Family.	A group of structurally related genera.
Fascicle.	A small bundle or compact cluster.
Fissure.	Small narrow opening or split.
Flange.	A rim or protruding edge.
Fungus.	Any of a group of plants comprising the molds, mildews, rusts, mushrooms, etc. They are destitute of chlorophyll and reproduce mainly by means of asexual spores.
Genera.	Plural of genus.
Genus.	A group of structurally related species.
Generic.	Pertaining to the genus or to the genera.
Glabrous.	Without hairs of any kind; smooth.
Globose.	Nearly globular; nearly round.

408

Glucosides.	Any compound which by hydrolytic decomposition yields sugar.
Heartwood.	Non-functioning woody tissue at the center of a tree trunk; generally darker in color than sapwood.
Herbaceous.	Non-woody.
High forest.	Virgin forest or any forest composed of normal timber-size trees.
Hyphae.	Fine thread-like strands of the body of the fungus.
Indigenous.	Native.
Kino.	Dark red or blackish tree product used in medicine and in dyeing.
Lagoon.	A small body of water near and communicating with the sea.
Lanceolate.	Narrow and tapering toward the end like the head of a spear.
Latex.	Milky fluid of certain trees from which rubber can be manufactured.
Leaflet.	A single blade of a compound leaf.
Lenticel.	A pore in the bark of a woody plant for the passage of air.
Liana.	Any climbing plant that roots in the ground.
Lichen.	Plant which grows on an epiphyte on rocks, bark, etc. It is a composite organism consisting of a fungus living symbiotically with an alga.
Lignification.	The process by which lignin, a cementing substance, is deposited in the wall of wood cells.
Liverworts.	A group of plants related to and resembling the mosses.
Maritime.	Bordering on or living near the ocean.
Membranous.	Resembling a membrane (used of an unusually thin leaf).
Midrib.	Continuation of the petiole through the blade of the leaf.
Mucilaginous.	Moist and viscid or sticky.
Oblanceolate.	Inverted lanceolate; with the broad end at the top.
Obovate.	Inverted ovate; with the broad end toward the top.

409

Obovoid.	Same as obovate.
Open crown.	Sparse foliage or few and widely spaced branches.
Orbicular.	Spherical or circular.
Ovate.	Egg-shaped with the broader end downward.
Ovoid.	Same as ovate.
Palmate.	Leaflets originating at a common point at the end of the petiole.
Panicle.	Any pyramidal, loosely branched flower cluster.
Parenchyma.	Soft woody tissue functioning for food storage; usually appearing light in color on a cross-section.
Pedicel.	A slender stalk.
Peduncle.	Flower stalk or stem.
Pericarp.	Ripened and modified walls of the flower ovary.
Petiolate.	With a petiole.
Petiole.	Stem of a leaf.
Pinnate.	Having leaflets arranged along each side of a common central axis.
Pithy tissue.	Tissue similar to pith; soft tissue; non-woody.
Pome.	A fleshy fruit, e.g. apple.
Pore.	A vessel as it appears in cross-section.
Pubescent.	Covered with short, soft, down-like hairs.
Pungent.	Causing sharp sensation of taste or smell.
Purgative.	When taken internally, acts as a cathartic or violent physic.
Quarter-grain.	Radial surface.
Raceme.	An inflorescence with flowers attached at intervals to an elongated axis.
Racemose panicle.	Panicle consisting of two or more racemes.
Radial surface.	Surface of wood along a vertical plane from the outside to the center of the tree.
Ray.	A ribbon-shaped formation of horizontal wood tissue extending at right angles to the growth rings.
Saponin.	Any of a group of glucosides occurring in many plants as in the soap bark tree and characterized by their production of soapy lather.

Sapwood.	The functioning woody tissue beyond or outside the heartwood. It is generally lighter in color.
Schizorcarp.	A dry fruit which opens in several segments.
Second growth.	The forest vegetation which occurs on an area after the original forest has been removed.
Second story tree.	A tree which is over-topped by the main crown canopy.
Sedative.	Tending to calm, moderate, or assuage pain.
Sessile.	Without peduncles.
Sinuous.	Bending in or out; serpentine or wavy form.
Sp.	Abbreviation of species. When used following the name of a genus, as "*Ficus, sp.*", it indicates an unidentified species of the genus.
Spp.	Plural of sp.
Species.	A group of trees possessing common, distinct structural characteristics which are constant in succeeding generations.
Tomentose.	With long curled matted hairs; woolly.
Teredo.	One of the marine wood borers.
Translucent.	Almost transparent.
Tylosis.	Intrusive growth from one cell into the cavity of another, sometimes forming there an irregular mass of cells.
Unarmed.	Without spines or thorns.
Vessel.	A large tube-like cellular structure in wood for water conduction.
Whorled.	Arranged in the form of a circle around a central axis.
Xerophytic.	Adapted to dry conditions.

411

REFERENCES

1. Ahern, G. P. The Uses of Philippine Woods. Bul. No. 11, Bureau of Forestry, Philippine Islands. Manila, 1911.

2. Ahern, G. P. and H. K. Newton. Bibliography on the Woods of the World. Scientific Contribution No. 10, Tropical Plant Research Foundation, Washington, D.C., 1928.

3. Anonymous. Forest Resources of the Philippines. Dept. of Agriculture and Commerce, Commonwealth of the Philippines, Manila, 1939.

4. Anonymous. Characteristics of Modern Woods. Second Edition, Roddis Lumber and Veneer Co., Marshfield, Wisconsin, 1939.

5. Anonymous. A Dictionary of Names Applied to Trees of the First, Second and Third Groups. Bul. No. 23, Bureau of Forestry, Philippine Islands, Manila, 1923.

6. Anonymous. Flora of the Solomon Islands. *Bulletin of Miscellaneous Information,* Royal Gardens, Kew, pp. 211-215, 1894, pp. 132-139, 1895, London, England, 1894-1895.

7. Blake, S. F. and A. C. Atwood. Geographical Guide to Floras of the World — Part I, 336 pp., Miscel. Pub. No. 401, U. S. Dept. of Agriculture, Washington, D. C., 1942.

8. Bourke - Burrowes, D. R. S. Teak Industry of Siam. Royal Forest Dept., Ministry of Commerce and Communications, Bangkok, Siam, 1927.

9. Brown, W. H. and A. F. Fischer. Philippine Mangrove Swamps. Bul. No. 17, Bureau of Forestry, Philippine Islands, Manila, 1918.

10. Brush, W. D. Teak (*Tectona grandis*). *Foreign Woods Series,* Forest Service, Dept. of Agriculture, Washington, D. C., 1937.

11. Burkill, J. H. Dictionary of the Economic Products of the Malay Peninsula. 2 Vols., 2,400 pp., 1935.

12. Burn - Murdoch, A. M. Trees and Timbers of the Malay Peninsula — Part I, Apr., 1911; Part II, Dec., 1912, Dept. of Forestry, Federated Malay States, Kuala, Lumpur, 1911-1912.

13. Burtt, B. L., Melanesian Plants, I. *Bulletin of Miscellaneous Information,* Royal Gardens, Kew, No. 5, pp. 298-306, London, 1935.

14. Champion, H. G. and Sir Gerald Trevor. Manual of Indian Silviculture. Oxford University Press, 1938.

412

15. Clarke, S. H. A Comparison of Certain Properties of Temporate and Tropical Timbers. *Tropical Woods,* No. 52, pp. 1-11, Dec., 1937.

16. de Clerq, F. S. A. Nieuw Plantkundig Woordenboek voor Nederlandsch Indie met Korte Aanwijzingen van het Nuttig Gebruik der Planten en Hare beteekenis in het Volksleven en met Registers der Inlandsche en Wetenschappelijke bemamingen. 395 pp., Amsterdam, 1909.

17. Cox, H. A. A Handbook of Empire Timbers. Forest Products Research, Dept. of Science and Industry Research, England, 1939.

18. de Dalla Torre, C. G. and Harms, H. Genera Siphonogamarium ad Systema Englerianum Conscripta. Lipsiae, Sumtibus Guilelmi Engelmann, 1900-1907.

19. Desch, H. E. The Forests of the Malay Peninsula and Their Exploitation. *Malayan Forester,* Vol. 7:4, pp. 169-180, Oct., 1938.

20. van Eeden, F. W. Houtsoorten van Nederlandsch Oost-Indie; Tevens Beschrijving der Meest Bekende Boomen van den Nederlandsch-Indischen Archipel en Hunne Waarde voor de Huishouding. 341 pp. Haarlem, 1905 (1906).

21. Endert, F. H. Forest Conditions and Timber Reserves in the Netherlands Indies. 5th Proceedings, Pacific Science Congress, Vol. 2, pp. 1013-1019, Univ. of Toronto Press, Toronto, 1933-1934.

22. Espinosa, J. C. Comparative Strength Properties of the Principal Philippine Commercial Woods. *Philippine Journal of Science,* Vol. 33, May-Aug., pp. 381-394, 1927.

23. Espinosa, J. C. Strength Properties in Relation to Specific Gravity of Philippine Woods. *Philippine Journal of Science,* Vol. 36, May-Aug., pp. 55-69, 1928.

24. Forest Research Institute, Buitenzorg, Java. Woods of The Dutch East-Indian Archipelago. International Critical Tables of Numerical Data, Physics, Chemistry, and Technology (8 vols.), Vol. 2, pp. 35-36, McGraw-Hill Book Co., Inc., New York, 1933.

25. Foxworthy, F. W. Commercial Timber Trees of the Malay Peninsula. *Malayan Forest Records,* No. 3, Federated Malay States Gov't., 1927.

26. Foxworthy, F. W. Commercial Woods of the Malay Peninsula. *Malayan Forest Records,* No. 1, *Malayan Science Bulletin,* Federated Malay States Gov't., April, 1921.

413

27. Foxworthy, F. W. and H. W. Wooley. Durability of Malayan Timbers. *Malayan Forest Records,* No. 8, Federated Malay States Gov't., 1930.

28. Foxworthy, F. W. Minor Forest Products of the Malay Peninsula. *Malayan Forest Records,* No. 2, Federated Malay States Gov't., Mar., 1922.

29. Foxworthy, F. W. The Almaciga Tree: *Agathis alba* Lam. *The Philippine Journal of Science,* Vol. V, No. 3, Sect. A, May, 1910.

30. Gamble, J. S. A Manual of Indian Timbers. 856 pp. Sampson, Low, Marsdon & Co., London, 1902.

31. Guppy, H. B. The Solomon Islands and Their Natives. 384 pp., Swan, Sonnenschein, Lowrey & Co., London, 1887.

32. Heyne, K. Nuttige Planten van Nederlandsch Oost Indie. 3 vols., 2nd Ed., Ruygrok & Co., Batavia, 1927.

33. Hooker, J. D. Flora of British India. 7 vols., L. Reeve & Co., Convent Garden, London, England, 1875.

34. Howard, A. L. A Manual of the Timbers of the World. 3rd Ed., 751 pp., MacMillan & Co., Ltd., London, England, 1948.

35. Hunt, G. M. and G. A. Garratt. Wood Preservation. 457 pp., McGraw-Hill Book Co., Inc., New York, 1938.

36. Jolly, N. W. Notes on the Principal Timbers of Queensland. Forestry Bul. No. 2, Dept. of Public Lands, Queensland, Australia. Brisbane, 1917.

37. Jolly, N. W. The Structure and Identification of Queensland Woods. Forestry Bul. No. 1, Dept. of Public Lands, Queensland, Australia. Brisbane, 1917.

38. Julius, G. A. Western Australian Timber Tests, 1906; The Physical Characteristics of the Hardwoods of Western Australia. Australia. 1918.

39. Kanehira, Ryozo. An Enumeration of Micronesian Plants. *Journal of the Dept. of Agriculture,* Kyushu Imperial University, Vol. 4, pp. 237-464, 1935.

40. Kanehira, Ryozo. Anatomical Characters and Identification of Formosan Woods. Bur. of Productive Industries, Gov't. of Formosa, Taihoku, 1921:

41. Kirtikar, K. R. and B. D. Basu. Indian Medicinal Plants. 2 vols., Sudhindra Nath Basu, M. B., Panini Office Bhuwaneswari, Asrama, Bahadurganj, 1918.

42. Koorders, S. H. and T. Valeton. Atlas der Baumarten von Java. 4 vols. (Illus. only), Buch- und Steindruckerei, Von Fa., P. W. M. Trap., Leiden, 1913.

43. Kraemer, J. H. Native Woods for Construction Purposes in the Western Pacific Region. 382 pp., Bureau

of Yards and Docks, Dept. of the Navy, Washington, D. C., 1944.

44. Kraemer, J. H. Native Woods for Construction Purposes in the South China Sea Region. 277 pp., Bureau of Yards and Docks, Dept. of the Navy, Washington, D. C., 1945.

45. Kurz, S. Forest Flora of British India. 2 vols., Office of Sup't. of Gov't. Printing, Calcutta, 1877.

46. Lam, H. J. Materials Toward a Study of the Flora of the Island of New Guinea. *Blumea,* Vol. 1, pp. 115-159, 1934.

47. Lane-Poole, C. E. The Forest Resources of the Territories of Papua and New Guinea. Commonwealth of Australia, Victoria, 1925.

48. Lauterbach, Carl. Beiträge zur Flora von Papuasien I-XXIV. *Bot. Jahrbuch Engler,* Vol's 40, 49, 52, 54-63, 66-70, 1912-1939.

49. Lecomte, M. H. Flore Generale de l'Indo-Chine. 5 vols., Masson et Cie, Paris, 1907-1931.

50. Lecomte, M. H. Atlas des Bois de l'Indo-Chine. 254 pp. Agence Economique de l'Indo-Chine, Paris, 1919.

51. Lee, Shun-Ching. Forest Botany of China. 991 pp., The Commercial Press, Ltd., Shanghai, 1935.

52. Markwardt, L. J. and T. R. C. Wilson. Strength and Related Properties of Woods Grown in the United States. Tech. Bul. No. 479, Dept. of Agriculture, Washington, D. C., 1935.

53. Merrill, E. D. A Bibliographic Enumeration of Bornean Plants. *Journal of the Straits Branch, Royal Asiatic Society,* Spec. Number, 637 pp., 1921.

54. Merrill, E. D. A Dictionary of Native Plant Names of the Philippine Islands. Bur. Gov't. Lab. Philippine Islands, No. 8, Manila, 1903.

55. Merrill, E. D. An Enumeration of Philippine Flowering Plants. 4 vols., Bur. of Science, Philippine Islands, Manila, 1925.

56. Merrill, E. D. Dermatitis Caused by Various Representatives of the Anacardiaceae in Tropical Countries. *Jour. American Medical Association,* Vol. 124, pp. 222-224, Jan., 1944.

57. Merrill, E. D. Emergency Food Plants and Poisonous Plants of the Islands of the Pacific. Technical Manual No. 10-420, Dept. of War, Washington, D. C., 1943.

58. Merrill, E. D. The Vegetation of Malaysia. *The Far Eastern Quarterly,* Vol. 2, No. 1, Nov., 1942.

59. Merrill, E. D. and L. M. Perry. Plantae Papuanae Archibaldianae. *Jour. of the Arnold Arboretum.*

60. Meyer, Hans. Buch der Holznamen. 4 pts., M. & H. Schaper, Hanover, Germany, 1933-1936.

61. Osborn, Fairfield. The Pacific World. 218 pp. W. W. Norton & Co., Inc., New York, 1944.

62. Pearson, R. S. and H. P. Brown. Commercial Timbers of India. 2 vols., 1,134 pp., Central Publication Branch, Gov't. of India, Calcutta, 1932.

63. Prilleux, Edouard. Sur les Productions Agricoles et Forestieres des Possessions Hollandaises des Indes Orientales. *Bul. Soc. Acclim. France,* III, 1, Vol. 21, pp. 359-389, 1874.

64. Rechinger, Karl. Uber eine botanische Forschungsreise nach den Samoa — und Solomoninselin; Einen Vortag am Versammlung am 26 Oktober, 1907. *Mitteilungen des Naturwissenschaftlichen Vereines fur Steiermark,* Vol. 44, pp. 244-254, 1908.

65. Reyes, L. J. Philippine Woods. 536 pp., Tech. Bul. No. 7, Dept. of Agriculture and Commerce, Commonwealth of the Philippines, Manila, 1938.

66. Reyes, L. J. Woods of the Philippine Dipterocarps. *Philippine Journal of Science,* Vol. 22, No. 3, pp. 291-344, Mar., 1923.

67. Ridley, H. N. Flora of the Malay Peninsula. 5 vols., L. Reed & Co., Ltd., London, 1922-1925.

68. Robson, R. W. Pacific Islands Yearbook. Pacific Publications, Pty., Ltd., Sydney, Australia, 1942.

69. Rodger, Alex. A Handbook of the Forest Products of Burma. Sup't. of Gov't. Printing, Rangoon, Burma 1921.

70. Schneider, E. E. Commercial Woods of the Philippines: Their Properties and Uses. Bul. No. 14, Bureau of Forestry, Philippine Islands, Manila, 1916.

71. Shaw, Norman. Chinese Forest Trees and Timber Supply. T. Fisher Unwin, 1914.

72. Smith, A. C. Studies of Papuasian Plants, I-V, *Jour. of the Arnold Arboretum,* Vol. 22, pp. 60, 231, 343 & 497; Vol. 23, p. 417, Harvard University, 1941-1942.

73. Swain, E. H. F. A Universal Index to Wood. Forestry Bul. No. 7, Queensland Forest Service, Dept. of Public Lands, Queensland, Australia, 1927.

74. Troup, R. S. The Silviculture of Indian Trees. 2 vols., 783 pp., Oxford at Clarenden Press, 1921.

75. Watson, J. G. Mangrove Forests of the Malay Peninsula. *Malayan Forest Records,* No. 6, Federated Malay States Gov't., Singapore, 1928.

76. Whitford, H. N. The Forests of the Philippines: Part I, Forest Types and Products; Part II, The Principal Forest Trees. Bul. No. 10, Bureau of Forestry, Philippine Islands, Manila, 1911.

INDEX TO BOTANICAL AND LOCAL NAMES
OF TREES

418

419

423

425

426

428

433

436